Nuffield Primary Science
SCIENCE PROCESSES AND CONCEPT I

G000066852

Science Co-ordinators' Handbook

PUBLISHED FOR THE NUFFIELD–CHELSEA CURRICULUM TRUST BY COLLINS EDUCATIONAL

NUFFIELD PRIMARY SCIENCE
Science Processes and Concept Exploration

Directors
Paul Black
Wynne Harlen

Deputy Director
Terry Russell

Project members
Robert Austin
Derek Bell
Adrian Hughes
Ken Longden
John Meadows
Linda McGuigan
Jonathan Osborne
Pamela Wadsworth
Dorothy Watt

Other contributors to the Handbook
Marcella Armstrong
Jo Frost
Elizabeth Harris
Brenda Keogh
Stuart Naylor
Anne de Normanville

Editor of the Handbook
Derek Bell

Safety adviser
Peter Borrows

Published 1996 by Collins Educational
An imprint of HarperCollins*Publishers*
77–85 Fulham Palace Road
Hammersmith
London W6 8JB

Based on the Nuffield Primary Science *Teachers'
handbook* first published 1993
Science Co-ordinators' Handbook first published 1996
Reprinted 1996 (twice)

The SPACE Project and the Trust are grateful to the
governors, staff and pupils of all the trial schools. It will
be obvious to readers of these publications how much
we are indebted to them for their help, and especially
for the children's drawn and written records of their
hard work and their growing understanding of science.

ISBN 0 00 310089 8

Design by Carla Turchini and Derek Lee

Printed and bound by Martins the Printers, Berwick on Tweed

Contents

To the Co-ordinator

The role of a science co-ordinator is central to the quality of teaching and learning in science in your school and is geared towards improving experiences and opportunities for children throughout the school. The role involves many different tasks: developing a policy; managing resources; keeping an eye on safety issues; monitoring children's progress throughout the school; and implementing and evaluating curriculum developments to meet the needs of the children and the demands of the National Curriculum.

This book does not discuss all aspects of the role; rather, it aims to support your curriculum development in science based on the SPACE approach and using Nuffield Primary Science.

The Nuffield Primary Science *Science Co-ordinators' Handbook* is designed to help you to:

◆ understand the basis of the SPACE approach;
◆ introduce and develop the SPACE approach in your school;
◆ provide support for you and your colleagues in adopting the SPACE approach to the teaching and learning of primary science;
◆ encourage the effective use of the Nuffield Primary Science publications in the classroom.

The handbook does this by providing:

◆ discussion of the underlying philosophy of the SPACE approach;
◆ practical guidance on planning and procedures for work in the classroom;
◆ suggestions for in-service work with colleagues;
◆ responses to some of the questions you may be asked by your colleagues as they use the SPACE approach and the Nuffield Primary Science publications.

The SPACE approach

Why adopt the SPACE approach?

A primary teacher has a very difficult task in teaching science effectively alongside all the other subject areas. To do it well, he or she has to keep the requirements of the National Curriculum in mind and:

1 decide what ideas children should be helped to grasp
2 decide what ways of developing science skills children should work on
3 select and design activities which attract children, which can be managed in the classroom, and which help achieve 1 and 2 above
4 make it all work on the spot.

The SPACE project is based on research done with and through teachers during extensive trials in schools. It will help you in the following ways.

◆ The ideas are clearly set out; they are based on research and trial, so we can be confident that children can grasp the targets chosen.
◆ The ways of working proposed help children use observation and testing to develop their own ideas and their skills.
◆ The Nuffield Primary Science books set out tried and tested activities with examples of pupils' work which have been shown to work to get to targets 1 and 2 above.

You have the classroom skills – the Nuffield Primary Science materials help you to go in well prepared and with clear targets.

You will have your own reasons for adopting the SPACE approach, but there are three particularly good reasons why it will help to bring about effective teaching and learning in science.

1 Recognition of the importance of children's own ideas

In a primary classroom where the SPACE approach to science is being used, the children are deeply involved in work which is based on their own ideas and they have taken part in deciding how to do it.

By deliberately finding out about the children's ideas, taking them seriously and choosing appropriate strategies for helping the children to test their ideas, the teacher moves children towards ideas which have wider application and fit the evidence better – which are, in short, more scientific. Working in this way, children do the changing, rather than simply accepting ideas they are told are better; and they advance their skills and ways of relating ideas to evidence.

2 The findings of a major research project

The SPACE (Science Processes And Concept Exploration) Project, funded by the Nuffield Foundation, was set up in September 1986 as a collaborative project between teachers, teacher advisers and researchers at Liverpool University (Centre for Research in Primary Science and Technology) and King's College, London.

The research, which was carried out with the teachers in their classrooms, looked at a wide range of concepts to find out:

◆ children's ideas about aspects of the world around them;
◆ how they came to form these ideas;
◆ the possibilities of helping children modify their ideas, to bring them closer to more useful, scientific ones.

The findings provide a fascinating account of the ideas children use to explain the scientific aspects of things around them, and how these ideas differ with their age and experience. Many children independently came up with the same ideas to explain things, so it was possible to describe ideas that might be expected in general from other groups.

The SPACE research reports describe the results of this research; they are listed in the Appendix.

The findings were also used to develop trial materials which helped teachers to plan activities so as to take children's ideas as a starting point in classroom work. The evidence provided the basis for the aims proposed and the methods suggested in the Nuffield Primary Science teachers' guides.

3 Support from publications

The Nuffield Primary Science publications are a resource for helping teachers put the SPACE approach to teaching and learning science into action in their classrooms.

The Nuffield Primary Science teachers' guides (see also pages 7, 16 and 19)

These provide activities for finding out children's ideas and ways of helping children develop their ideas. Additional support for the teacher is provided through the inclusion of planning suggestions and background science.

The Nuffield Primary Science pupils' books

These are intended for use as a supplement to classroom work. They are available to enrich the pupils' work in science in the ways described below and on page 19.

There are 33 pupils' books, 22 linked in pairs with one pair to each teachers' guide at age range 7–11 (Key Stage 2), and one to each teachers' guide at age range 5–7 (Key Stage 1). Each is at the appropriate reading level for the age range intended. (For the linked pairs at 7–11, one is aimed primarily at lower juniors – Years 3 and 4 – and one at upper juniors – Years 5 and 6.)

In each pupils' book there are eleven double page spreads which may be a short story, or a poem, or a series of photographs. The content of the spreads are not usually linked to one another – the books can be dipped into whenever the content seems useful. Suggestions are made in the teachers' guides when the pupils' books can be used to support an explanation. The topics have been chosen to match the interests of both girls and boys, and care has been taken to emphasize multi-cultural aspects and equal opportunities.

The Nuffield Primary Science in-service pack

The pack consists of four units, each covering a particular aspect of the SPACE approach, and contains:

◆ a number of workshop activities for teachers;
◆ suggestions for running the workshop activities;
◆ background notes for the course leader and participants;
◆ OHP masters of photocopiable notes and diagrams.

The materials can be adapted to meet the needs of practising teachers and students in initial teacher training, and as part of school curriculum evenings for parents. Each course should attempt to:

◆ establish the nature of the SPACE approach;
◆ consider the importance of finding out children's ideas, and encourage teachers to try the different techniques with their own classes;
◆ look at ways in which children can be helped to develop their ideas.

Organization of Nuffield Primary Science teachers' guides

Age range 5–7 (Key Stage 1)

Chapter 1 Planning
The SPACE approach to teaching and learning science
Useful strategies
Charts to help children develop their ideas
The themes and the curriculum
Experimental and Investigative Science
Planning your science programme in school
Planning a topic: case study
Resources
Pupils' books
Warnings

Chapter 2 Exploring the themes of the guide
For each theme:
Areas for investigation and Key ideas
A look at ...
Finding out children's ideas: starter activities
Children's ideas
Helping children to develop their ideas

Chapter 3 Assessment
Examples of assessment in operation: matching evidence of achievement with the National Curriculum level descriptions

Age range 7–12 (Key Stage 2)

Chapter 1 Introduction
The SPACE approach to teaching and learning science
Useful strategies
Equal opportunities
Themes and the curriculum
Experimental and Investigative Science

Chapter 2 Planning
Introduction: planning with children's ideas in mind
Cross-curricular topics
Topic plan examples
Use of information technology
Pupils' books
Planning your science programme in school
Resources
Warnings

Chapter 3 Exploring the themes of the guide
Theme organizer
For each theme:
Areas for investigation and Key ideas
A look at ...
Finding out children's ideas: starter activities
Children's ideas
Helping children to develop their ideas

Chapter 4 Assessment
Examples of assessment in operation: matching evidence of achievement with the National Curriculum level descriptions

Chapter 5 Background science
Explanation of the scientific view of contents included in the guide

CHAPTER 2

Introducing Nuffield Primary Science into the school

Getting started

If you are introducing a scheme into your school, remember that:

◆ the process will take time, especially if your colleagues are not familiar with the approach or the materials;
◆ you need to familiarize yourself with all of the materials and the underlying philosophy of the approach;
◆ a whole school approach, with the head teacher's support and the sharing of experiences, is likely to be the most effective.

Exactly how you introduce the materials into your school will be determined by your own situation. The relations you have with your colleagues will be particularly important. The following is one way you might approach your task.

Informal discussions

Show some of your colleagues the books and see whether they find them interesting and valuable. This will help you gauge the general feeling and reaction to Nuffield Primary Science, and will involve them in decision-making.

Staff meeting

Spend about an hour introducing the SPACE approach and showing how Nuffield Primary Science supports it. Use copies of the OHP masters given in this chapter. The other chapters of this handbook provide further details that might be helpful.

◆ Use the OHP 'The SPACE approach to teaching and learning science' (see page 9) to help you describe the approach, emphasizing that it starts by using children's ideas. (5 mins)
◆ Give out some examples of children's work. You could either gather some from your own class or use the examples given here (see pages 10–14). Ask your colleagues to consider:
  – how the children might have come to hold these ideas;
  – what could be done to help the children think about their ideas and help them to develop a more scientific view. (15 mins)
◆ Discuss their responses in general terms. (5 mins)
◆ Use the OHP 'Support for planning in the Nuffield Primary Science teachers' guides' (see page 15) to help you introduce the Nuffield Primary Science materials and show how the teachers' guides help to support the SPACE approach. (10 mins)
◆ Allow time for everyone to look at the teachers' guides and pupils' books and consider how they might use them in planning their next topic. (15 mins)
◆ Ask everyone to plan a suitable 'starting activity' from a theme in one of the guides and to try it out with their class before the next meeting. (10 mins).

This meeting could be followed with one to look at some of the ideas that

The SPACE approach to teaching and learning science

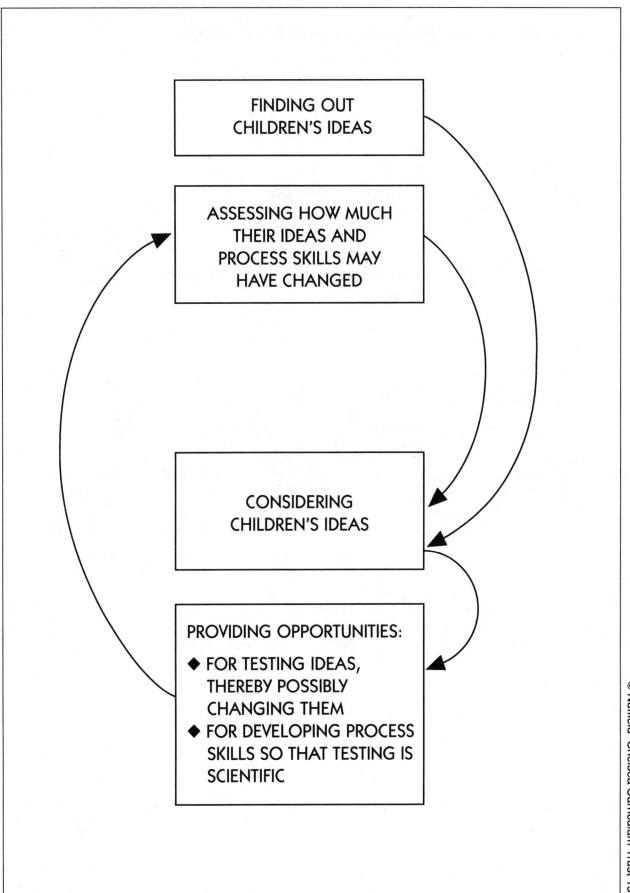

FINDING OUT
CHILDREN'S IDEAS

ASSESSING HOW MUCH
THEIR IDEAS AND
PROCESS SKILLS MAY
HAVE CHANGED

CONSIDERING
CHILDREN'S IDEAS

PROVIDING OPPORTUNITIES:

◆ FOR TESTING IDEAS,
THEREBY POSSIBLY
CHANGING THEM
◆ FOR DEVELOPING PROCESS
SKILLS SO THAT TESTING IS
SCIENTIFIC

Draw pictures of all the different things you can think of which give light.

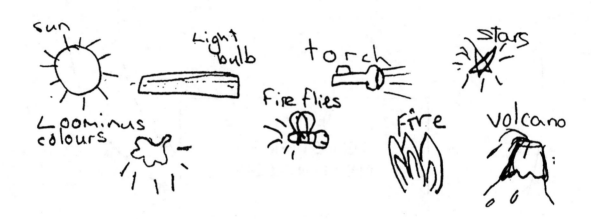

Draw a picture to show how you can see the candle/book.

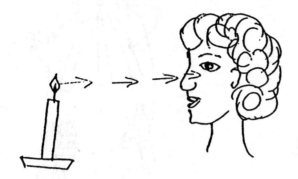

What do you think happens to the food inside your body?

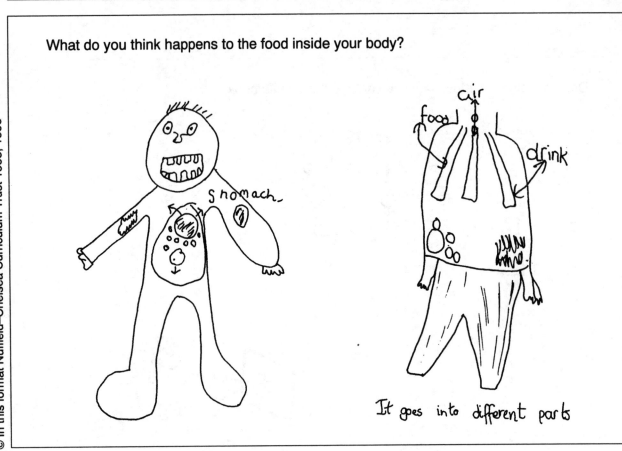

It goes into different parts

What do you think your body is like inside?

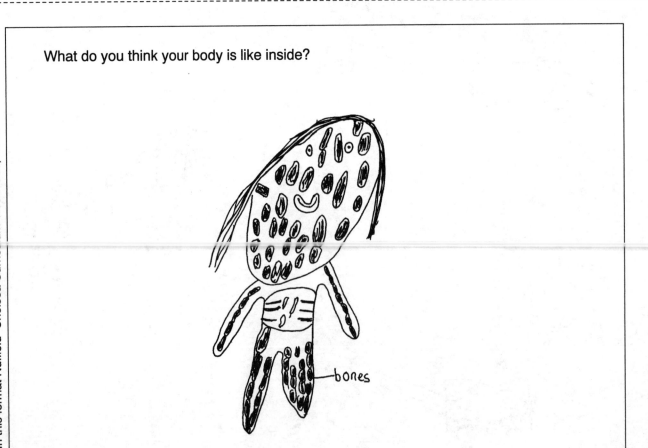

Draw a picture of what you think is inside an egg.

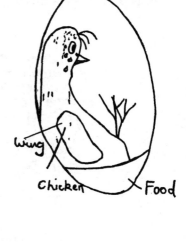

What do you think a plant needs to grow well?

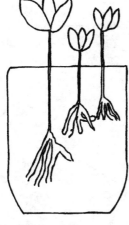

These are broad beans. They need water to live.

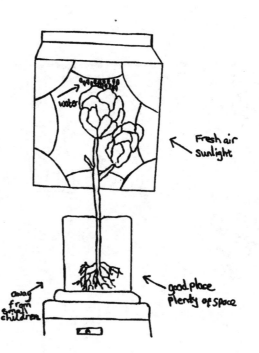

Fresh air
Sunlight

good place
plenty of space

away from small children

How do you think this toy works?

Your power (human power) is where the enegry comes from that is when you push down the toy.

spring that pushs a bar

The enegry from human power is then tranfered in to the spring where it makes the toy work because enegry is stored in the spring.

Bar that when you push the toy the toy pushes the spring and the springpushes the bar and then the bar turns a cog. the big cog turns a small cog which turns another cog then that turns the wheel.

the key that you wind it up with

white thing in the middle of the train that spins around

thats the engine

← the sun

people in the train

the holes that you put petrol in

(The bottom drawing is annotated by the teacher.)

Support for planning in the
Nuffield Primary Science teachers' guides

The teachers' guides include:

 Planning chapter containing:

- ◆ suggestions for topics
- ◆ worked example of a topic plan, highlighting the science and links to other areas of the curriculum
- ◆ examples of whole school plans
- ◆ list of resources
- ◆ description of the pupils' books linked to the themes in the guide
- ◆ notes about safety and other sensitive issues

 Key scientific ideas and suggestions for areas of investigation at the beginning of each theme

 Simple background science

 Links with the National Curriculum Programmes of Study

 Each theme gives:

- ◆ ideas for ways of finding out children's ideas, with suitable questions
- ◆ examples of typical ideas expressed by children during the research
- ◆ suggestions for helping children to develop their ideas
- ◆ chart of responses to children's ideas related to the theme

 Assessment chapter which uses examples of children's work to suggest the kinds of evidence which show the level at which the child is working

have been found and to discuss ways of helping children to develop their ideas. Encourage everyone to work together in groups to plan their next topics, using the teachers' guides, and to discuss the work as it progresses.

An INSET or planning day

This is an example of how you might use one of your training days, following a staff meeting similar to that described above.

Use the OHP 'The SPACE approach to teaching and learning science' (see page 9) to remind everyone of the elements of the approach. Then use the OHPs 'Techniques for finding out children's ideas' and 'Techniques for helping children to develop their ideas' (see pages 17, 18) to consider the different ways of finding out ideas and helping children to develop them.

Examine how the teachers' guides might be used.

Working in planning groups, use the teachers' guides to prepare the next topic to be taught. The following points should be considered in each case:

◆ the concepts and parts of the programmes of study to be covered;
◆ possible starting points and specific starting activities;
◆ the anticipated responses children might make;
◆ the key ideas the children are being helped to understand;
◆ how to cope with the responses (given that we know that many are predictable);
◆ activities, based on the anticipated responses, that might be used to help children develop their ideas;
◆ opportunities for assessment;
◆ resources.

The chart given on page 24 of this book might be used as a framework for recording plans. The 'flow diagrams' given in each theme of the teachers' guides are also useful in planning.

Ask each planning group to present a summary of their plans to the rest of the staff.

Discuss some of the issues that need to be considered when implementing the SPACE approach. (The chapters in this book and the activities described in the *In-service pack* will help you structure this part of the day.) Examples might be:

◆ the role of science process skills and practical activities;
◆ identifying progression in children's ideas;
◆ identifying opportunities and planning for assessment.

Additional staff meetings or planning days could be used to develop or revise your whole school plan to ensure coverage of the curriculum and to make links with the teachers' guides in a similar manner to the examples given on page 22 and in the teachers' guides.

Using the Nuffield Primary Science teachers' guides

The use of any curriculum materials is a personal matter. It depends on your own experience and background, the children in your class and the school situation. The need for flexibility and adaptability has been taken into consideration in designing the Nuffield Primary Science teachers' guides.

Techniques for finding out children's ideas

Listening to what children say and watching what they do

◆ one-to-one discussions

◆ small group discussions

◆ class discussions

◆ children-only group discussions

◆ sorting activities

Encouraging children to put ideas on paper

◆ annotated drawings/diagrams

◆ sequenced drawings

◆ structured writing

◆ log books

Techniques for helping children
to develop their ideas

Enabling children to test their own ideas

◆ using process skills in an investigation to see if the evidence fits their prediction

Encouraging generalization from one context to another

◆ using a concept to explain different but related events

Discussing the words children use to describe their ideas

◆ recognizing that words may have different meanings in different contexts and learning to distinguish between them

Extending the range of evidence available

◆ seeking further evidence, particularly for events which are difficult to observe directly

Getting children to communicate their ideas

◆ giving opportunities to think through their own ideas and to interact with others' ideas

Structure of the teachers' guides

All guides are arranged in a similar pattern and include the following:

◆ Introduction to the SPACE approach;
◆ Suggestions for planning work involving the science covered in the guide;
◆ Suggestions for ways of using the pupils' book materials;
◆ 'A look at ...' at the beginning of each theme gives a description of the scientific concepts and understanding children could be expected to develop by the end of primary education, through the study of that particular theme;
◆ 'Key ideas': these are important aspects of the scientific concepts covered by the theme. Some might be understood during primary education, while others may not be comprehended until later. Even in the latter case, however, children may begin to develop their understanding of them. Key ideas are not specific points to teach. Rather, they provide information to guide you in helping children to develop their ideas;
◆ Specific suggestions of ways to find out children's existing ideas. The activities and techniques included are based on those that were found to be successful during the research phase of the project;
◆ A description of the children's ideas that were identified during the research studies, and of how these ideas help to show development of the concepts involved in working towards the accepted scientific view;
◆ A collection of strategies, ideas and activities that have been found helpful in encouraging and challenging children to reassess their ideas in the light of their new experiences;
◆ Guidance on assessing skills relating to AT1 and children's ideas as part of the teachers' interaction with them;
◆ Background information on the scientific ideas explains the subject matter of the guide.

Working with the guides

Initially the guides might be used to follow a pattern involving:

◆ gaining familiarity with the SPACE approach and the scientific concepts being considered, using Chapter 1 and the Background science;
◆ identifying which aspects of the science contained in a guide are relevant to broader themes or topics, so that the work can be related to the curriculum as a whole;
◆ identifying the key ideas the children are being helped to understand;
◆ referring to the appropriate theme(s) in a guide and selecting suitable activities for finding out children's ideas;
◆ using the children's ideas section to help anticipate children's responses;
◆ plan ways in which children's ideas may be further developed through practical activities, vocabulary, and generalizations related to the concepts involved;
◆ making reference to appropriate sections of the teachers' guides as required, such as the 'Assessment' chapters.

Using the pupils' books

The pupils' books can be used to support or start small-group activity among pupils. For example, some photographs such as the optical illusion pictures in *Light* serve as starting points linked to a teachers' guide topic, and are useful for arousing curiosity or provoking questions for discussion. Others can be the basis for other kinds of activity – paper and pencil games, picture completion or matching activities – which might serve to revise or consolidate classroom learning.

Some of the material provides sources of information that might be used for work on a particular theme, for example on *The Earth in Space*, or about animals for work on *The variety of life*. Such information is provided in a variety of ways: pictures or photographs with discussion points, puzzles, or short pieces giving interesting facts and figures.

More generally, the pupils' books present material that is designed to be interesting to read, or to look at as a basis for discussion. Such pieces might be used as links with work in other subject areas. For example, stories in which a science idea was a key to the plot can be used for reading development as well as for consolidating science work; a spread on the everyday applications of science, or about 'how it works', can be a starting point for work on identifying needs and opportunities in Design and Technology; a piece on a historical aspect of science can make a link with work in History.

Overall, the books are a resource that can be used flexibly as an aid for learning; in particular, they are of value in the organization of work that children can do on their own or in small groups, so that teachers can devote themselves to discussions with one or a few pupils at a time.

Planning for science: a whole school approach

The Nuffield Primary Science curriculum materials have been designed to allow schools and teachers to incorporate science in their curriculum in a way that meets their needs. Science may be included:

◆ as part of integrated topics, where work in science and other curriculum areas such as maths, English, history, geography, art, technology, music etc. are carried out as they arise;
◆ through the study of more restricted science-based topics, where science may lead to activities in other subjects;
◆ as specific science sessions where the activities have their own cohesion, independent of work in other areas.

With regard to topic work it is useful to keep in mind the caution pointed out by HMI in their report *Teaching and learning: primary science* (DES 1989, paragraph 74):

> Some caution is needed about this [the topic] approach since the least effective work is often associated with topics where far too much is attempted and – as a consequence – too little is achieved in depth of knowledge, understanding and the acquisition of skills in the constituent subjects.

The Nuffield Primary Science materials help to avoid this situation by clearly defining the processes and concepts of science related to each of the themes.

Whole school plans

The development of a whole school plan helps to ensure that:

◆ children are given a breadth and balance of experience in science;
◆ concepts are revisited on a number of occasions, preferably in different contexts;
◆ all parts of the Programmes of Study are covered;
◆ due attention is given to issues of progression and differentiation.

The example of a whole school plan given on page 22 shows how one school has planned its curriculum for science.

Examples of whole school plans

The example given is not a definitive model, but is one stage in the development of a coherent programme for a school. It should be adapted to fit your own situation and preferences. The 'topics' given are only illustrative and may be taught individually as science or as part of a wider topic. There is a progression through the different elements of the PoS for Sc1, 2, 3 and 4. Each area of the PoS is addressed every year, and each element is visited once every two years. In addition, during years 3 to 6 the topic marked by an asterisk is the major one for the year and would be covered over a term, while the others would be covered in half a term.

Planning schemes of work

Consideration should be given to the points listed on page 23:

RECEPTION

	Me and my family	Our garden	My house	Toys	Stop, look and listen	Changing times
NPS 5–7 TG	Living processes The variety of life	Living things in their environment	Materials	Forces and movement Using energy	Light Sound and music	The Earth in Space

YEAR 1

	Living things	Seeds and flowers	Ourselves	Pushes and pulls	Bits and pieces	Sounds
NPS 5–7 TG	The variety of life	Living processes	Living processes	Forces and movement	Materials	Sound and music
PoS	Sc2: 3b, 4b, 5a	Sc2: 3a, 3c	Sc2: 1a, 1b, 2a, 2b, 4a	Sc4: 2a, 2b, 2c, 2d	Sc3: 1a, 1b, 1c	Sc4: 3c, 3d, 3e

YEAR 2

	Changing materials	Local habitats	Growing up	Lights	Using materials	Electricity and magnetism
NPS 5–7 TG	Materials	Living things in their environment Rocks, soil and weather	Living processes	Light	Materials	Electricity and magnetism
PoS	Sc3: 1a, 1b, 2a, 2b	Sc2: 5a, 5b	Sc2: 1a, 1b, 2c, 2d, 2e, 2f	Sc4: 3a, 3b	Sc3: 1c, 1d, 1e	Sc4: 1a, 1b, 1c

YEAR 3

	Fruit and vegetables	*Properties of materials	Shadows	Making sounds	Making things move
NPS 7–12 TG	Living processes	Materials	Light	Sound and music	Forces and movement
PoS	Sc2: 1b, 3a	Sc3: 1a, 1b, 1c, 1d, 2b	Sc4: 3a, 3b, 3d	Sc4: 3e, 3f, 3g	Sc4: 2a, 2b, 2d, 2e, 2f

YEAR 4

	Ponds and streams	*Humans and other animals	In the kitchen	Batteries and bulbs	Keeping healthy
NPS 7–12 TG	Living things in their environment	The variety of life	Materials	Electricity and magnetism	Living processes
PoS	Sc2: 5a, 5b	Sc2: 1a	Sc3: 2a, 2b, 2c, 2d, 2f	Sc4: 1a, 1b	Sc2: 2a, 2b, 2h

YEAR 5

	Growth of plants	Rocks and soil	Reflections	Changing sounds	*Changing and stopping movement
NPS 7–12 TG	Living processes	Rocks, soil and weather	Light	Sound and music	Forces and movement Using energy
PoS	Sc2: 3a, 3b, 3c, 3d	Sc3: 1d, 2a, 3a, 3b, 3c	Sc4: 3c, 3d	Sc4: 3e, 3f, 3g	Sc4: 2b, 2c, 2f, 2g, 2h

YEAR 6

	*Woodlands	Solids, liquids and gases	Earth and beyond	Switches and circuits	How the body works
NPS 7–12 TG	Living things in their environment	Materials Using energy	The Earth in Space	Electricity and magnetism	Living processes
PoS	Sc2: 4a, 5b, 5c, 5d, 5e	Sc3: 1e, 2d, 2e, 3d, 3e	Sc4: 4a, 4b, 4c, 4d	Sc4: 1b, 1c, 1d	Sc2: 1a, 2c, 2d, 2e, 2f, 2g, 2h

- the key ideas which are being addressed and the most appropriate context in which to investigate them;
- the activities which will encourage children to think and express their ideas about the concept being explored through the topic;
- the possible ideas that children might express;
- the provision of opportunities for children to develop the skills and processes of science alongside their understanding of the concepts;
- the nature of and possibilities for assessing and recording children's progress;
- classroom organization and management, including any safety considerations.

On the next page is an example of how such planning might be organized.

Are there opportunities for unified teaching of National Curriculum subjects?

While the National Curriculum is specified in terms of subjects, it does not follow that these subjects have to be, or even ought to be, taught in isolation from one another. There are many common elements which might well be treated together. Some examples are :

- The emphasis on communication skills in the Programmes of Study for Science means that some aspects of English are required in the teaching of science.
- The sections of the Programmes of Study for Mathematics on Handling Data and on Using and Applying Mathematics overlap strongly with elements of Scientific Investigation.
- The discussion in the Programmes of Study of Design and Technology and the reference there to the use of science in that subject again set out positive requirements for overlap.

What are the advantages and disadvantages of teaching science within a cross-curricular topic?

If electricity is introduced as an activity involving children in connecting light bulbs, batteries and wires, it will interest some children. It would become much more meaningful, and interest more children, if it were set in the context of a project in which they were involved, such as a working model of a fairground or a model theatre. Both of these projects would provide opportunity for cross-curricular work in addition to the science.

Children also need to be clear about the purpose of the scientific activities in which they are involved. For this to happen, their work in science has to relate to their everyday lives and to the ideas they already have. If children have a genuine problem to solve, such as making a working model of a lift with a pulley system for Design and Technology, they will have a clearer idea of what pulleys are for and how they work than if they learnt about them in isolation.

Children need also to learn to draw on the scientific knowledge they have. Cross-curricular topics can help provide opportunities for children to apply their knowledge and skills in a variety of contexts. For example, in a topic on litter, children may think about how rubbish is recycled and use their knowledge of magnets and the properties of materials to work out how iron and steel may be separated from other materials. Or, in a topic on the Victorians, children may think about how food was preserved and use their knowledge of micro-organisms to suggest how this might have been improved.

PLANNING A TOPIC: MATERIALS AND THEIR USES

Creating the climate

Teacher tasks	Children's involvement	Core activities	Assessment	Classroom organization
Provide stimuli – questions	Children bring in materials	Interactive materials display	Gain initial ideas from children	Set up display area
Set context	Children explore materials available		• log book	Provide materials (with children's safety in mind)
Consider own thoughts on concepts	Record/discuss general thoughts		• discussion (class and individuals)	Make time for children to interact with display
Familiarize with PoS and ATs				Arrange for collecting ideas

Finding out ideas

Teacher tasks	Children's involvement	Core activities	Assessment	Classroom organization
Decide emphasis for investigation	Children carry out activities	Selection of starter activities	Determination of existing ideas on properties of materials (note others)	Provision of materials (with children's safety in mind)
Find out children's ideas	Record using e.g. annotated diagrams and lists	e.g. to consider properties of materials	Match to ATs where appropriate	Arrange children in groups
Identify starting activities			Note demonstration of skills especially observations	Determine times for activities to be carried out
Prepare exploratory activities			Record responses	

Helping children to develop their ideas

Teacher tasks	Children's involvement	Core activities	Assessment	Classroom organization
Help/guide children in investigations	Devise and carry out tests on materials	Exploring the properties of materials	Note skills of:	Provision of likely resources (with children's safety in mind)
Introduce additional ideas	Identification of similarities and differences		• hypothesizing	
Question			• predicting	Arrangement of resources
Consider lines of development			• measuring	
Provide supplementary activities			• planning and carrying out investigations	Determination of group size and timing of activities
			• recording and ideas emerging	

Concluding the topic

Teacher tasks	Children's involvement	Core activities	Assessment	Classroom organization
Note areas covered	Bring findings together	Presentation of findings	Confirmation/ clarification of points with individuals	Prepare space for display of findings
	Prepare report	• display		Arrange time for class discussion
		• class discussion		

To sum up, if science can be taught within a cross-curricular context, you can:

◆ draw on a range of interests and backgrounds so that more children will be fully involved;
◆ give children a sense of purpose in their science work and help them to relate it to their everyday life;
◆ help children to apply their scientific knowledge in a variety of contexts, enabling them to make generalizations about scientific ideas.

The main pitfalls to watch out for when teaching science within a cross-curricular topic are:

◆ the science may become lost among the many other activities and therefore lose its focus; this has happened in the past when the scientific aspects of a broad-based topic appeared on planning charts, but in practice became a minor feature of the work;
◆ the topic may cover a number of aspects of the PoS so that no one area of science is covered in any depth; children's learning will at best be superficial; and children may become confused when faced with learning several different concepts at the same time;
◆ it can be difficult to monitor children's conceptual development within a particular domain.

How can Nuffield Primary Science materials help in planning schemes of work?

Each teachers' guide and pupils' book follows the content of particular aspects of the PoS. Comprehensive coverage of Sc2, Sc3 and Sc4 comes from using the ideas from several guides. Sc1 is an integral part of each teachers' guide. The table on page 40–41 shows how Sc2, Sc3 and Sc4, and the strands within them, are related to the teachers' guides for ages 5–7 and 7–12. Within each guide the activities are set out so that you have the maximum flexibility to use the ideas to fit your own preferred way of working.

You should regard the material in the guides as a kit of parts to be assembled in your own design of a curriculum. You can present science to children as part of an integrated topic, as part of a science-based topic, or as a specifically science topic. You may well use all three modes at different times.

When selecting suitable topics for cross-curricular work, you might start with the area of science which is to be covered and think about topics in which it may be applied or to which it could be relevant. Alternatively, it may be more productive to think first of other topic or subject areas, and to see how science ideas and skills can be included in the work.

What is to be done about Information Technology?

Children should become familiar and confident with the various aspects of information technology through using it in the work on various subjects when opportunities arise. Examples include databases and data handling, keys and other identification programmes, sensing equipment for measuring light and sound intensity, and secondary source material on CD-ROM.

Throughout the teachers' guides guidance is given on how information technology might be incorporated into activities. In your own schemes of work, you may find opportunities both to apply information technology experience acquired in Science to subsequent work in other subject areas, and to use work initiated in other areas to Science.

Implications of the SPACE approach for classroom organization

The research phase of the SPACE project involved finding out children's ideas and then helping them to develop these ideas. Whilst there are useful parallels between the research and teaching, it is helpful when using the Nuffield Primary Science materials to be aware that there are also important distinctions. Some of these are listed below.

◆ The SPACE research was able to focus on individual children's ideas. Teachers do not usually have the time to do this.

◆ The SPACE research allowed teachers to find out children's ideas, to reflect on them and then to offer suitable opportunities for the children to develop them. Teachers often have to work much faster, with less time for reflection between finding out and helping to develop the children's ideas.

◆ The SPACE research gave teachers the chance to allow children to devise investigations that they thought would be the best way to test their ideas. There were no obvious restrictions on the kinds of investigation that were possible. However, teachers often have to plan activities in advance and stick to whole school schemes of work.

◆ The SPACE research team was able to analyse carefully a range of possible targets for the ideas children could develop, but the teacher only needs to know which of these were found to be practicable and important.

If teachers are not aware of these differences between research and teaching, they may conclude that the approach adopted in the SPACE research sounds fine in theory but is unrealistic in practice. Teachers need to be confident and realistic in what they aim to achieve through their teaching. Some pointers are therefore given to help you and your colleagues develop the SPACE approach in your classrooms.

You may not be able to explore each individual child's ideas, but eliciting these is still worthwhile. Getting the children to make their ideas public is an important step in clarifying them, and can help them realize the need to develop them further. Sharing ideas in a class or group can help children realize that others think differently, which can show them that they need to find out more. So eliciting children's ideas is useful for the children themselves, not just for you. You need not feel guilty that you cannot find out as much as you would like about the ideas of individual children.

Many of the activities suggested in the Nuffield Primary Science teachers' guides can help to link the discovery and the development of children's ideas. For example, class or group discussion can be a useful way of finding out more about what children think. Skilful and challenging questioning during the discussion can also cause some of them to change their views, so that they are already developing their ideas.

Although certain activities may be prescribed in a school scheme of work, this does not mean that children's ideas cannot be taken into account. Often it is possible to anticipate the kind of ideas that the children are likely to have; the teachers' guides are useful here. You can then foresee what activities are likely to be suitable and what resources ought to be provided.

For example, one teacher was planning some work on shadows. She planned to begin by asking the children to look at their shadows in the playground and then draw their shadows when they came back into the classroom. She was able to use the ideas in the *Light* teachers' guide, ages 5–7, pages 26–28, to anticipate that some of the children would draw shadows that were upside down, or coloured, or had features such as eyes and mouths, or which were not attached to the body.

She could see that a follow-up activity that involved more careful and systematic observation of the shadows formed by objects (*Light* teachers' guide, ages 5–7, pages 34–38) would enable all the children to develop their ideas further. Even though this activity was set out in the school scheme of work, the children's ideas could still be taken into account.

Using the SPACE approach in the classroom

The SPACE approach can be employed in various ways, provided that the organization allows its essential features to be put into practice. At various times there has to be opportunities for:

◆ teachers to listen to children speaking, in a one-to-one situation, in small groups and in whole class discussions;
◆ children to discuss things with their teacher and with other children;
◆ children to explore real things and express their ideas about them;
◆ children to try out their ideas in practical investigations.

As long as curriculum organization makes these things possible, the SPACE approach imposes no restrictions, although some arrangements will certainly make this easier. For example, it is important for children to have a chance to talk to other children about their work and to exchange ideas. In this way they learn that there are alternatives to their own ideas and become more ready to look at things from a different viewpoint. This is possible only if children have shared similar experiences, at least as starting points for their activities.

One pattern of organization might be as follows.

Preparation

You will have planned carefully and clearly identified the key ideas that children are being helped to understand.

Initial stimulus

Allow the children to observe a large block of ice or ice balloon, in groups or as a whole class. Encourage them to raise their own questions, which will provide a basis for further exploration. You can also raise questions to focus the children's thinking and help to reveal their ideas, such as 'Why do you think the ice is melting?' or 'How do you think you could stop the ice from melting?' This will give you a chance to introduce ideas, experiences and observations which are felt to be important in helping the children to develop understanding of the concept, in this instance that of change of state from solid to liquid.

Finding out the children's ideas

You can use a group or class discussion to gather all the children's ideas. It is important that this encourages the children to express their ideas, by treating all their ideas as valuable. Open questions will form an important part of the discussion. Although class discussions are easy to organize, they can sometimes be so interesting that teachers feel they spend too long on them, so that science becomes more talked about than actively experienced. Some children may also be reluctant to contribute when in a large group.

Alternatively, the children could produce a short piece of writing or annotated drawings to record their ideas. Either of these could be produced by individual children or groups. You might produce a large chart or display, with individual children or groups contributing their ideas in turn.

Helping the children develop their ideas

The children will have a wide range of ideas about the ice, its properties and what happens to it over time. They will probably have raised lots of questions and possibilities for further investigation, such as 'What happens if you put salt on it?' 'What does it look like in the middle?' 'What happens if you put it in water?'

You will probably feel that some of these questions are unlikely to be productive. However, trying to focus the children's attention and restricting their thinking at this stage is likely to be a mistake. As adults we usually want to explore before we form theories; children feel this even more strongly. It will be more useful to provide some time (and resources where necessary) for the children to explore at least some of their ideas.

This can lead to further group or class discussion, and possibly the production of some writing or work for display.

This would be a suitable moment to bring the children's attention back to the question of how the ice could be kept from melting. Their earlier explorations will provide a useful background for a more focused investigation. Their ideas can be listed, and they can be encouraged to devise investigations to test these. As they plan their investigations you should be able to listen to and interact with individual children or groups. This will be a valuable opportunity to find out more about the children's ideas and to respond to them with suggestions, questions and challenges that will help them to develop their ideas further. In this way finding out and developing children's ideas become part of an ongoing process.

You will need a supply of ice cubes for the children to test their ideas; ice cubes are much easier to make and to handle than ice balloons. Would putting an ice cube in a glove make it melt faster or more slowly? Would wrapping one in aluminium foil speed up or slow down melting? Such ideas can readily be investigated. The children's ideas will be very different, but they can be tested and developed by broadly similar activities.

In other words, finding out and using children's ideas does not always mean having completely different activities for each child. It does mean that activities can be provisionally planned as part of a whole school scheme of work, in the knowledge that they will be suitable ways of developing ideas. The key to making activities productive is for children and teachers to be clear about their purpose.

Reflection and consolidation

At intervals during the learning cycle, children should be encouraged to think about their ideas again. Asking them to consider how their ideas have changed will help children recognize and consolidate their deeper understanding.

You should also reflect on the ideas expressed by children in order to assess their progress and to decide on subsequent activities.

How should groups be organized?

Sometimes it can be useful to group the children according to the ideas that they express. This allows close links between their ideas and the follow-up activity. It can also be helpful for ensuring differentiation. Evidence from the SPACE research indicates that the main ideas in a class recur, so there will probably not be too many groups.

However, grouping the children according to their ideas may cause problems. It is not how most teachers normally work, so it can disrupt classroom routines. It may be difficult to manage in some circumstances, such as small schools with vertically grouped classes. Finding out children's ideas, for example through discussion, can also cause their ideas to shift, so that it is impossible to make up suitable groups.

Fortunately, grouping children according to their ideas is not always necessary. There is research evidence which suggests that children can gain more from interacting in groups with other children whose views are different from theirs. The range of ideas put forward can stimulate all the children to think through and justify their views more fully than they otherwise would.

A period of open exploration as described above can be a useful starting point for helping children to develop their ideas. Sometimes this may be followed by a common investigation which all the groups carry out, such as the one on shadows described earlier (see pages 26–27). Sometimes there may be a common theme, but individuals or groups can investigate different factors and then discuss their findings with the other children. An example is the investigation into parachutes in the *Forces and movement* teachers' guide for ages 7–12, page 48. Some children might choose to test their ideas about the effect of the shape of the parachute, while others investigate its size, the length of the strings, the weight attached and so on.

Whether all the groups do science at the same time depends on the classroom circumstances and your preferred method of organization. Some teachers feel more confident directing their attention to a single curriculum area, though children may carry out different activities within that area. Other teachers feel that directing most of their attention to one or two groups is more effective, with other groups engaged in activities that require less teacher support. Some activities, such as engaging the children's interest or sharing ideas, may be most suitable as a whole class activity. For other activities, such as challenging the children's ideas or devising investigations, it might be necessary to plan to spend time with specific groups.

Differentiation: providing suitable learning opportunities for all children

One of the most difficult issues to deal with in organizing learning is that of differentiation: matching activities and experiences to the needs of individual children. There is no easy solution to this problem, but it is possible to overcome many of the difficulties by using knowledge of children's ideas to provide new experiences that are within reach of children's existing ideas and skills.

This can be approached in two stages.

1 Plan activities pitched at the general level you would expect children to have achieved at this point in their development. This is helped by using the examples of children's ideas given in the teachers' guides, and by knowledge of the children in the class.
2 By paying careful attention to the ideas expressed by individual children working on the same activity, it is possible to 'fine tune' the experience for each child. Sensitive use of questions and suggestions encourages children to think about their own ideas, and challenges them to test them in different ways. This may lead to some children being left to work things out for themselves, while other children are given more support to help them move ahead with their thinking and process skills.

The first stage takes place when preparing your whole school plan and schemes of work for each term or half term. The second stage will be catered for when planning individual lessons and during the activities.

Case studies

Each teacher, class and classroom is unique, so that the way in which the SPACE approach is implemented will differ in detail; but each teacher will be helping the children develop their ideas. The two case studies that follow are therefore only examples of how two teachers in two different schools have approached the challenge.

Classroom organization for ages 5–7 (KS1)

A large primary school in north-east England is the setting for this first example. In the first half of the autumn term the two Year 2 classes, which are run in parallel, were looking at 'humans as organisms' through a theme of 'Giants'. The 70 children in the two classes worked an integrated day in mixed-ability groups and the theme was linked closely to Maths work.

The children started by making two large figures of giants, during which many of the Maths ideas (measuring, capacity and number work) were developed. These figures became a significant part of the children's lives during this time.

The children were then asked to think about the giants and asked to make annotated drawings in response to questions such as:

◆ What do you think a giant is like inside?
◆ Does a giant have bones?
◆ How do you think a giant moves?
◆ Can you draw a giant's finger?

These drawings were used as the starting points for discussions with the children about themselves, by encouraging the children to think about how they are the same as a giant and how they differ.

Science was going on at all times alongside Maths and English. This gave the teacher the opportunity to work or sit with different groups, listening to them, encouraging them to think about their ideas and suggesting ways in which they might test these.

In the Giants topic there is a lot of 'grouping', looking for similarities and differences. (See *The variety of life* and *Living processes* teachers' guides.) Each group tended to investigate different ideas such as height, eye colour, leg length, and shoe size. They recorded their work, which was brought together into one big wall display and used as a focus for children to reflect on their findings. The children explained their findings and compared them with those from other groups. Children were then encouraged to think of other questions that had arisen from their findings; these questions were also added to the display.

Classroom organization for ages 7–12 (KS2)

This study is from a junior school in a semi-rural area of South Wales. The children are grouped by ability for Maths and language, but all other subject groupings are much more flexible depending on the topic. This helps greatly in Science because it means that it is possible to delay the choice of working groups until after an initial brainstorming session.

The Year 3 class started their topic 'Ourselves' by observing each other, looking for similarities and differences. (See *The variety of life* and *Living processes* teachers' guides.) This lead to a class discussion, which initially drew up a list of the observations the children had made but then developed into a question raising session. The large number of questions generated made it impossible to answer them all, so the children had to decide which should be investigated. This meant that the children had to start to recognize different types of question. Some were followed up by individual children using secondary sources, including the Nuffield Primary Science pupils' books.

It was agreed that they should investigate two questions:

◆ Does gender affect head size?
◆ Does age affect head size?

Working in friendship groups, the children tested their responses to one of the questions. Initially each group put their ideas with the reasons for them on a chart, which provided a record of their understanding at the start of the work. Some groups used tape measures for their investigation, some used rulers. Others tried hats of different sizes on children aged eight, nine and ten. Two groups wanted to measure the head size of all the eight-year-old boys and all the eight-year-old girls. This involved going into other classes, so pairs worked in a convenient space outside the classroom and pooled their information.

Towards the end of the first investigation session the class came together to talk about what they were doing. This gave an opportunity to discuss the suitability of the methods that each group had selected for their investigation.

Further investigations were developed, with the class coming together frequently to report progress and discuss ideas which were then presented in a joint display.

Safety in science

Safety is of paramount importance, and you must consider it when planning for science. Any safety points should be identified in the scheme of work, and should be a part of short-term planning and classroom organization. Classroom helpers (whether support staff or parents) need to be made aware of any safety issues.

Teachers may not adopt suitable precautions simply because they are not familiar with an activity, or because they are unaware of possible safety implications. For example, some people are allergic to the spores produced by moulds, and so if children are to observe mould growing on bread, after initial exposure to the air the bread should be enclosed (but not totally sealed) in a plastic bag. Similarly, the hazards of mixing different types of battery may be unexpected and thus not be appreciated.

In planning activities, teachers must follow any local code of practice or safety guidance produced by the employer, that is the local education authority or governing body. The Department for Education (now the Department for Education and Employment) and the Welsh Office have endorsed *Be safe! Some aspects of safety in school science and technology for Key Stages 1 and 2* (2nd edition 1990, Association for Science Education, College Lane, Hatfield, Herts, AL10 9AA; telephone 017072 67411) as providing suitable guidance on safety in science for primary schools. Many LEAs have adopted it as the basis for their code of practice for science, sometimes with additional notes or rules. (A separate Scottish edition of *Be safe!* was published in 1995.) Because there are sometimes unexpected problems, teachers should be aware of the scope and coverage of *Be safe!* and any local codes. The ASE publishes an INSET pack for use by science co-ordinators, *Safety in science for primary schools* (ASE, 1994) which would help to raise awareness. In addition, nearly all local education authorities, and many grant-maintained and independent schools, are members of the CLEAPSS School Science Service, Brunel University, Uxbridge, UB8 3PH; telephone 01895 251496. Their *Primary science and technology newsletter* sometimes includes safety matters, and they produce (free) guides of direct safety relevance, for example on electrical safety and on the use of household chemicals. There is also a Helpline which is free to members.

In Nuffield Primary Science, activities which need particular care are indicated by this symbol in the margin. Each teachers' guide lists points requiring particular attention. However, do not assume that no reference necessarily means that there are no possible hazards – it can be difficult to foresee what some children will do. Hence there is a need to be familiar with *Be safe!* and similar guidance. It is essential that pupils' plans are checked by the teacher before they start work, but equally teachers need to be vigilant during an investigation, as plans are often changed as the work proceeds.

There is more to safety than simply telling children not to do something and restricting activities to those accepted as safe. Teaching safely is not the same as teaching safety. The preamble to the Programme of Study for Key Stages 1 and 2 in the (1995) National Curriculum (sometimes referred to as 'Sc0') includes a requirement that pupils should be taught about various aspects of health and safety, including recognizing and assessing hazards, and taking steps to control risks. They should be helped to recognize dangers to themselves and others, and reduce the risks from them not only in the work they do in class, but also in the home, on the street or in the park.

The following is not an exhaustive list of safety points, but may serve as a reminder about some of the more common or serious problems. It is no substitute for the more detailed guidance referred to above. There is a need for particular vigilance with younger children.

With young children (or with older pupils with learning difficulties) one of the main problems is a tendency to put everything into their mouth or other orifice. Some young children have died as a result of swallowing pen tops or bottle tops. So avoid small, tempting objects, such as the very small 'button' batteries. Expanded polystyrene, often used as packaging, is not suitable for classroom use by young children: some LEAs and schools have banned it in infant classrooms. The problem is that it can be squashed quite small and poked into an ear, say, where it expands to such an extent that it can be very difficult to remove. This can also happen with cotton wool, but less severely.

Avoid small sharp objects such as pins – screws and nails are safer.

Some schools or LEAs will not allow glass in infant classrooms. This is not just a matter of thermometers, but also containers such as jam jars. Plastic soft drinks containers, cut down and with any sharp edges taped, can be used as transparent containers. For smaller volumes, disposable plastic beakers may be useful. Bear in mind that plastic containers may melt or soften if hot water is put into them. One child got burnt when near-boiling water was poured into a plastic cup, which softened and collapsed.

Take particular care with thermometers. If, with older children, you do use glass thermometers avoid those containing (silvery) mercury, because it is toxic. (If a mercury thermometer does break, do not panic, there is no immediate danger to health. For advice on clearing up a mercury spill contact the CLEAPSS Helpline, or a neighbouring secondary school.) Alcohol thermometers (containing red, blue or green liquid) are safer, but will break if put into near boiling water. Thermostix, digital thermometers, liquid crystal thermometers and temperature probes connected to a computer are alternatives, but reading the temperature with such instruments is a different and less demanding skill.

When working out of doors beware of the risks of infection, for example from tetanus in the soil and from dog mess. Even apparently clean grass can infect children with *Toxocara canis* if they put fingers in their mouth. Any cuts should be covered with a waterproof plaster before going outside, and hands should be washed on return. If taking children on farm visits, ensure there are facilities for washing their hands.

When using food (for example in taste testing or cooking) take great care with hygiene. Explain to pupils what is necessary and why, so that they gain an understanding which they may apply at home as well. Similarly, with the risks of burning during heating or cooking activities.

Some chemicals can be safely used by children, although any substance is harmful if taken in sufficient quantity. DO NOT assume that because something is easily available at home it must be safe. It is often NOT, and children need to be taught this.

Children need to be taught the safe way to use tools, including scissors. Care needs to be taken when flying kites or balloons, or when testing parachutes, catapults, ballistas and mangonels.

Batteries are safe to use, but different types should not be mixed and they can get very hot if they discharge quickly as a result of being short-circuited. Work using batteries is a good opportunity to teach pupils about the dangers of mains electricity 'We use batteries for work on electricity because they are safe ...'.

The teacher's role

What role do I have in the SPACE approach?

In the SPACE approach children's ideas form the key to their learning, and their activity is a basis for developing those ideas. However, these features do not mean that the teacher's role is a passive one; on the contrary, the teacher has an active and central role in the child's learning. Throughout, the teacher must be clear about the targets towards which it is hoped the children will move. To this end you must be able to identify which ideas the children should develop. The five main aspects of that role are as follows:

1 finding out what children's ideas are;
2 reflecting on how children may have arrived at their existing ideas and how far they have progressed towards developing more scientific ideas;
3 helping children to develop process skills so that they test and apply their ideas scientifically;
4 providing opportunities to test or challenge ideas, perhaps leading to changes;
5 assessing the extent of any change in ideas and in process skills which may have resulted.

These are not isolated aspects of teaching. The third and fourth are interwoven parts of the same process of teaching and learning, for if children do not develop rigorous ways of testing their ideas they may see no need to change them in the light of their evidence. The first and fifth aspects are likewise closely linked. The first may be a distinct step at the beginning of a new topic but, as the topic activities proceed, the last step of assessing change becomes the first step in subsequent activities. Finally, the second aspect pervades most of the work, as a teacher develops understanding of a child and decides how to guide that child.

The diagram on page 9 represents these aspects on a simple version of the cyclic model of teaching used in the SPACE approach. The different aspects will be important at different stages of children's learning. This chapter simply gives an overview; Section B (see page 42 onwards) offers more detailed guidance.

What is my role in finding out children's ideas?

The key to your role at this stage is to respond, accept and explore the child's ideas – and, above all, to be non-directive. The idea of standing back to avoid suppressing certain ideas and imposing others may be unfamiliar to some teachers. The temptation to intervene and correct wrong or confused ideas may be very strong if one is used to instructing pupils.

While it is non-directive, the role is not passive. Careful listening has to go along with careful questioning designed to encourage children to explain their ideas and to give the teacher as full a picture as possible of their thinking. Reflection on the answers is essential if follow-up questions, and associated activities, are to be framed to open up the children's communication. You can read more about this in Section B.

What role do I have in encouraging children to develop their ideas?

Here the second, third and fourth aspects in the list at the start of this chapter are all involved. Your role has to change from one of inquiring in a non-directive way to one of provoking, challenging and questioning. Children will not necessarily have personal reasons to reconsider their ideas unless they encounter a new experience or situation which makes it necessary or interesting.

It follows that your first task is to make sure you are clear about the direction in which children's learning should go. Activities for children which will lead them to think again are set up to help move them in this direction. Such activities have to be chosen after considering the evidence of the ideas that children already have. Each of the teachers' guides contains tried and tested ideas for its topic.

Your role here will still be more subtle than one of telling the children what they should think or believe. Essentially, it is to make sure that they are careful and thorough in collecting and thinking about new evidence. It also involves making sure that they give reasons to support their ideas, and can plan and carry out investigations to test them. The degree of guidance will depend on children's responses, but children should be encouraged as far as possible to feel that they are working with their own ideas.

Your role is again an active one, requiring skill in judging when and how to intervene. You have to know both the child's starting point and the destination – the more scientifically useful idea. You have to guide pupils so that they make their own path towards scientific ideas and do so by developing their science skills.

What are the other aspects of the teacher's role?

Assessment must be an integral part of the teaching and learning process. Finding out what children's ideas are is one stage in the programme of formative assessment. As one activity is completed and another one planned, formative assessment will again be an essential feature.

Finally, you will have to organize and plan so that the various stages — finding out children's views, setting up classroom activities to explore and challenge children's thinking, and assessing their progress – all take place within a coherent scheme of work and in relation to children's other learning activities.

What do teachers need to know?

Many teachers feel that their own grasp of science ideas is inadequate. They may have had an unhappy time with science when they were at school, and that experience may have left them with a belief that science involves ideas that are so obscure that they cannot hope to understand them. As a result, they believe that they will be quite unable to explain those ideas to their pupils.

Each of the teachers' guides for ages 7–12 includes a background science chapter written to help teachers with the knowledge and understanding of science ideas that they will require for the topics involved. This section explains how these requirements fit in with the SPACE approach, and emphasizes two main points. First, the ideas we want primary children to learn have been shown by research to be well within the grasp of any primary school teacher. Second, the ways in which children should be encouraged to approach these ideas are fully consistent with good primary practice in other areas of the curriculum.

How similar are scientists' science and children's science?

There should be a great deal of similarity between the way scientists work and the way children can learn science. In both, the ideas held before an investigation influence the way the task is understood and approached. However, scientists' existing ideas come from the powerful base of knowledge and concepts built up over centuries and learnt through training and experience. Children's ideas come from everyday experience, from the language and ideas of adults and peers, and from their own ways of making sense of the world.

Children's learning should involve a close interaction between the *content* of science and the *processes*. Children cannot explore and change their ideas unless they can use and develop their powers of observation, of seeing regularities, of making and testing hypotheses. Consider an exercise in which children are asked to discuss the similarities and differences between various seashells. The child who knows where the shells come from and their role in the life of shellfish is likely to notice quite different features from those picked out by a child to whom they are simply decorative ornaments. For example, many shells that can be collected on a shore are half of the body case, others are the whole case. However, if you don't know that shells are body cases and therefore have an inside and an outside, you will not notice many features of biological significance.

Because process skills can only be exercised on some particular phenomenon or topic, the way children use them will depend on their existing ideas about the subject. Indeed, one important object of any learning activity should be to develop and change those ideas by using these processes. The SPACE approach allows close interaction between the content and process aspects, both in science itself and in the learning of science.

Are scientific ideas hard to grasp?

One reason why science has always seemed difficult to many people is that teaching has started by assuming that certain ideas about natural phenomena are obvious or easily grasped, though to young children they may not be obvious at all. Young children have their own ideas of how to explain things around them. If a science teacher gives them quite different explanations without evidence that they can understand, they may be confused and fail to see why their own ideas are inadequate or why they should change them.

A child might be told at home that you need exercise to build up your energy. If a teacher then says that exercise uses up energy, the child has a conflict to resolve. Children often resolve such conflicts by remembering to repeat what was learnt in school when asked in school, and using the home idea outside school.

Any successful approach to learning must take account of this. It also follows that the scientific ideas involved must be at a level that is not too demanding for teachers.

An example is the understanding of light. Many people who studied physics at school will say that this is a very difficult subject. They may have vague memories of lenses, ray diagrams, formulae in which the signs were governed by mysterious rules and only came out right if you worked backwards from the right answer, and things called virtual images which you could see but which were not really there. If they have to teach infant and junior children about light they may well start to worry.

However, some of the main ideas about light set out in the first levels of the National Curriculum are that:

◆ some materials are opaque and some are not;
◆ we only see things when light comes into our eyes.

The first is hardly ever taught at secondary level – it is 'obvious'. Yet to young children it is not at all obvious; the second idea has not been grasped even by many pupils who have studied physics up to age sixteen.

These ideas about light are stepping stones to more advanced ones; they form the basis on which later learning about light may progress, whether in the top juniors or in the secondary school. However, in themselves they are not complicated, and they do present interesting opportunities for work with everyday observations and simple equipment – torches, candles, mirrors, shadow puppets – in which children can develop both science process skills and skills of discussion and representation relevant to English and mathematics.

Another example illustrates a further important point. Many teachers may have been able to interest young children in observations and experiments involving colour. The scientific study of colour is complex, involving not only physicists' ideas about the spectrum and wavelength, but the physiology of colour perception which shows that what we 'see' depends on far more complicated factors than those considered by the physicist. Therefore many very simple observations on colour are hard to interpret, and it is almost impossible for children to build up a useful basis for concept development from everyday observations. Although work on colour is a rich source for discussion, observation and investigation with young children, it cannot profitably be taken much further as a basis for developing science concepts.

This illustrates a general point: part of the task of the teacher is to choose and recognize only those ideas and experiences which do provide opportunities to build up a useful basis for science concepts. The explanations of background science given in the teachers' guides for ages 7–12 serve to distinguish basic and relevant ideas from more complex ones.

The Nuffield Primary Science materials and the SPACE approach will help children develop the scientific concepts required by the National Curriculum at Key Stages 1 and 2. These ideas were chosen because they are accessible to young children, mainly through observations and simple experiments, and because they form the basis for later science learning. They should not present significant problems for primary teachers.

What do I do if I can't answer children's questions?

In the SPACE approach children are encouraged to express their ideas in an atmosphere of acceptance and encouragement. They should also try out their ideas, ask questions, and find out and bring ideas from a variety of sources; while all ideas may be challenged by experience or by social interaction. A teacher may have a good grasp of the main target ideas and of the reasoning behind the activities, but may not feel confident about questions or ideas that go well beyond that knowledge. For example, a child might ask: 'Why is the sky blue?' An explanation is quite complex and requires some notion of wavelength, which will not yet have been introduced.

It is possible for a naive inquirer to ask questions about the natural world that even an able scientist cannot answer, particularly not in simple terms. An example might be: 'Will the Universe go on for ever?' But there is no shame if a teacher has to say that she or he does not know the answer, particularly if this is followed by an attempt to treat the ideas seriously and discuss whether there is any evidence or test that could take them further. What does matter is that the response is completely honest. It helps if the teacher knows a reasonable amount about the science involved, but even the knowledgeable have to be careful. An answer that displays superior knowledge could close off the child's thinking, or even make the child think that his or her ideas look silly when set alongside the profound insights of real science. Thus a wise answer might use very little of one's background knowledge. The priority, for the scientifically learned teacher or for the novice, might be the same: to encourage the child's own powers of thinking and observing and investigating further.

In the teachers' guides, the explanations of scientific ideas are designed to set out the background of understanding needed in guiding children's learning in the Nuffield Primary Science themes. Teachers should not need to go beyond this.

How do I know if I'm doing a good job?

The following questions may act as a checklist of aspects of classroom life to which attention should be paid, and at the same time as criteria for evaluating them.

No formality is intended in these questions. They are to be used as is felt best, although you will need a reasonably systematic approach to get useful results from them. The questions are framed so as to be relevant in most classrooms, but not all will be appropriate for the youngest children. A positive answer is expected to each of them. If some answers are negative, teaching methods may need to be reconsidered. You might want to reread some chapters in the second half of this handbook; where relevant the chapter numbers are given in brackets.

The questions are in no particular order, and there is no suggestion that some are more important than others.

The first list applies to the children. When you are away from the children and have time to reflect, think back over the science activities for a particular week or two and ask yourself these questions. Don't accept the answer 'yes' too easily; make sure you can give a specific example that justifies the answer.

During this time, have children:

1 talked to each other in small groups about the things they were observing or investigating? [8]
2 talked freely to you about what they think? [7, 8]
3 shown and explained their work to others? [9]
4 listened to alternative ideas from others? [8, 9]
5 explained what they meant by a word? [9]
6 agreed with a different view from their own on the basis of sound argument or evidence? [8]
7 written down, drawn or made something that conveys their own ideas? [8]
8 asked questions which indicated their interest in the way they were working or what they were finding out?
9 handled materials, and made and expressed observations about them? [12]
10 carried out an investigation they had helped to plan? [9]
11 suggested ways of testing their ideas? [12]

12 expressed justified criticism of the way an investigation was carried out? [13]
13 used measurement in setting up or finding results from an investigation? [12]
14 asked questions which led to investigations? [12]
15 made a prediction based on their own ideas? [9]
16 linked observations in one situation to a relevant previous experience? [9]
17 shown absorption in their work or other signs that it is important to them?
18 used sources of information to answer factual questions? [9]
19 changed their ideas towards more accepted scientific ones? [14].

The second list applies to the teacher's thinking and behaviour. In the same period of time, have you been finding out children's ideas? That is, have you:

1 been aware of the children's ideas about the materials, objects and events being studied? [8]
2 asked the children questions which invited them to talk about their ideas? [8]
3 asked for writing, drawings or other products in which the children expressed their ideas about why something happened or behaved in a certain way? [8]
4 deliberately kept silent and listened to the children talking? [8]
5 made interpretations of the children's written or other products in terms of their ideas and skills? [8]
6 been aware of knowing something about the ideas of every child in the class in relation to the topic on which they are working? [8, 10].

Have you been helping children to develop their ideas? That is, have you:

7 provided opportunities for children to explore, play or interact informally with materials? [9, 11]
8 encouraged children to ask questions?
9 provided opportunities and encouragement for children to talk informally in groups? [9]
10 provided opportunities for children to present ideas or to describe their investigations to others? [9]
11 responded to questions by suggesting what the children might do to find out rather than providing a direct answer? [12]
12 noticed children working well without your help?
13 become aware of changes in children's ideas from ones previously held? [14]
14 provided sources of information for the children to find out more about a topic? [9]
15 challenged children to test and reassess their present ideas? [14].

Have you been personally surprised and interested? That is, have you:

16 found the topics being studied interesting and intriguing?
17 felt that your knowledge of the topics was sufficient?
18 been surprised at something the children have found out? [11]
19 been surprised by the ideas and skills shown by certain children? [11]

Nuffield Primary Science and the National Curriculum

Teachers' guide	Themes (ages 5–7)	Strands of the Programmes of Study at KS1 and KS2 of the National Curriculum	Themes (ages 7–12)
Living processes	2.1 How do we know if it's alive?	Sc2:1 Life processes	3.1 How do we know if it's alive?
	2.2 The human body and keeping healthy	Sc2:2 Humans as organisms	3.3 The human body
	2.3 Plant and animal growth	Sc2:3 Green plants as organisms	3.2 Keeping healthy
			3.4 Plants
Living things in their environment	2.2 Waste and decay	Sc2:3 Green plants as organisms	3.3 Waste and decay
	2.1 Habitats	Sc2:5 Living things in their environment	3.2 Feeding relationships between organisms
	2.3 Effects of human activity on the environment		3.1 Habitats and environmental change
			3.4 Effects of human activity on the environment
Variety of life	2.1 Naming and grouping living things	Sc2:1 Life processes	3.1 Classifying and identifying living things
	2.2 Individual variation	Sc2:4 Variation and classification	3.2 Individual variation
	2.3 Past life forms		3.3 Fossils and past life forms
Materials	2.1 Properties and uses of materials	Sc3:1 Grouping and (at KS2) classifying materials	3.1 Properties and uses of materials
	2.2 Changing materials	Sc3:2 Changing materials	3.2 Solids, liquids and gases
		Sc3:3 Separating mixtures of materials (KS2)	3.3 Changing materials

Teachers' guide	Themes (ages 5–7)	Strands of the Programmes of Study at KS1 and KS2 of the National Curriculum	Themes (ages 7–12)
Rocks, soil and weather	2.1 Rocks and soils 2.2 Weather	Sc2:1 Grouping and (at KS2) classifying materials Sc3:3 Separating mixtures of materials (KS2) Sc3:2 Changing materials	3.1 Rocks and soils 3.2 Weather
Using energy	2.3 Energy sources 2.1 Hot and cold 2.2 Mechanisms	Sc2:2 Humans as organisms Sc3:1 Grouping and (at KS4) classifying materials Sc3:2 Changing materials Sc4:2 Forces and motion	3.1 Energy sources 3.2 Hot and cold 3.3 Mechanisms
Electricity and magnetism	2.1 Sources and uses of electricity 2.2 Circuits 2.3 Magnets	Sc4:1 Electricity Sc4:2 Forces and motion Sc3:1 Grouping materials	3.1 Sources and uses of electricity 3.2 Circuits 3.3 Altering the flow of electricity 3.4 Magnets
Forces and movement	2.1 Pushes and pulls 2.2 Floating and sinking	Sc4:2 Forces and motion	3.1 Moving things 3.2 Stopping and staying put 3.3 Floating and sinking 3.4 Structures and balance
Light	2.1 Light sources 2.2 Reflections and shadows 2.3 Colour	Sc4:3 Light and sound	3.1 Light sources and vision 3.2 Reflections and shadows 3.3 Colour
Sound and music	2.1 Sound	Sc4:3 Light and sound	3.1 Making and receiving sound 3.2 Sound travelling
The Earth in Space	2.1 Time 2.2 Earth, Sun and Moon 2.3 Seasonal change	Sc4:4 Earth and beyond	3.1 Time 3.2 Day and night 3.3 The stars and the Solar System 3.4 Seasonal change

CHAPTER 7

Starting with children's ideas and knowing when to stop

Why do we need to start with children's ideas?

Science in the primary school, as elsewhere, is about developing an understanding of the world. It is concerned with the living and non-living materials in the world, and with understanding that is developed through testing ideas against available evidence.

Learning science is the gradual building of ideas, and of skills in testing them to see if they fit evidence from the world. The ideas children develop will necessarily be limited by their experience and by their still immature skills in testing them scientifically. It is the task of science education to extend their experience, to help them develop their scientific skills, and to help them relinquish ideas that are of restricted application in favour of more scientific ones. 'Scientific' in this context means not only fitting the available evidence but also enabling related phenomena to be understood.

When children's existing ideas are acknowledged, learning may be seen as the change in these ideas resulting from testing them against evidence, in much the same way as scientists test their theories. The change may involve modification of initial ideas, or rejecting them and adopting new ones that fit the evidence better. In any case the change has to be carried out by the child's own reasoning so that the new ideas become his or her own.

The same view of learning is expressed in various documents supporting the implementation of the National Curriculum. For example:

> Children arrive at school with ideas about natural phenomena and events in the world about them. ... It is very important to appreciate that children's preconceptions affect their thinking and interpretation of scientific events. As well as planning science lessons on the basis of skills, knowledge and understanding in the National Curriculum, it is essential to consider the children's starting points.
> (*Teaching science at Key Stages 1 and 2*, NCC 1993, page 36)

The reasons for finding out children's ideas and using them can be summarized briefly as follows:

◆ Using children's ideas reflects the way in which children learn naturally.
◆ Scientists themselves behave in a similar way. They use the ideas they have, and test them out to develop further understanding.

More pragmatically, consider what happens when children's ideas are not taken into account. Children do not give up their own ideas; they appear to hold on to them with a conviction that is not easily shifted. Therefore:

- The ideas the children express are sometimes contrary to what they have been taught.
- It is easy to make a wrong assumption about what a child knows.
- There is a danger that a child will come to see science as detached from his or her own personal views. Children may use a scientific idea to solve a specific problem without really believing in the idea they are applying.

How do children get ideas of their own?

A central tenet of the SPACE approach is that children have ideas about the world around them, about how and why things happen. These ideas are not only those that children have been taught but may also originate in the personal, physical experiences of the child. Thus, for example, some intuitive ideas about friction may be gained by trying to slide on different surfaces. Ideas constructed from such direct experiences are often particularly resistant to change. People and the media may be the source of other ideas. For example, advertisements showing cavemen beside dinosaurs may encourage children to believe that both lived at the same time.

Although the sum total of each child's ideas will be different in detail, since no two children will have had exactly the same experiences, this does not mean that the range of ideas on a particular topic will be infinite. Experience has shown that within a particular area children are likely to have had similar experiences and built up similar ideas to explain them.

What if children don't seem to have ideas?

With this rich background for the origin of ideas, at first sight it is surprising that children will say 'I don't know' when asked what they think. It is also a serious worry, because that is no basis for helping children to develop their ideas. It may take time for children not previously accustomed to expressing their ideas to develop the confidence to do it, and this is one of the most common reasons for a blank response. Other reasons may be:

- It may be an almost automatic response by a child who expects that all questions require a 'right' answer.
- It may also be a way of coping with a question the child finds threatening. A younger child with a short attention span may be temporarily more interested in something else. It would be appropriate to wait and ask the question again.
- The question may have come out of the blue. It is vital to provide real experiences before asking questions. This gives the child time to consider the matter in hand. It might also be appropriate to rephrase the question or to set it in a context which gives more time for response, by giving the opportunity to draw, for example.
- Similarly, the reply 'I don't know' may indicate that a child genuinely has not thought about the matter before. Although children will have worked out ideas on some topics, they are not likely to have preconceived ideas on everything. Here you might respond by encouraging the child to think it out, if that is appropriate. The child will need time to do this, and perhaps the opportunity to represent his or her thoughts by writing or drawing. If, as already suggested, questions follow experiences, more children are likely to have given some thought to the subject.
- Ultimately, however, there should always be the option of a genuine 'I

don't know' – one that implies '... but I want to find out'. This is a proper scientific attitude.

An absence of response at some stage in work on a topic may also mean that a place to stop has been reached.

How are children's ideas recognized?

In some cases children may have ideas but not communicate them in a way their teacher recognizes.

Some children cannot easily express what they think. Here you may be able to tease out thoughts and help in their formulation. Modes of expression other than speech may prove fruitful.

Younger children in particular may be unable to express their ideas. They tend to think in terms of action. When infants in one project school were given toy cars and a ramp, they rushed to see if the cars would go down the ramp without falling off. They did not seem interested in saying why the cars went down. Although they were clearly playing, there would have been ideas behind what they were doing.

It may also be possible to infer children's ideas from their actions. This is obviously difficult, but we should remember that the youngest children show evidence of thinking before they speak. Even babies show that they realize a ball is still there when it has rolled out of sight. They have an idea of the ball's permanence before they can put that idea in words.

Alternatively, in such a situation you may turn the questioning towards what seemed to govern the children's activity. They may be asked what made the cars go down the ramp instead of why they went down. If you are still set on finding out if a child has an idea of why the car goes down, the 'why' question may be made less threatening by different phrasing: 'Why do you think ... ?' or 'What do you think makes the car go down?' Some ways of phrasing questions are more productive than others in generating dialogue. Not only does the right question need to be asked, it needs to be asked at the right time. It may be better to give children the opportunity to play before asking for their ideas.

A further difficulty may be in recognizing what is meant by an idea. Some teachers who said that children did not appear to have ideas were perhaps looking for rather complex and theoretical concepts. Consider these answers to the question of why a toy car moves down a slope:

> It moves because of its engine.
>
> It moves because of its wheels.
>
> It moves because it is pulled downwards.

The third statement is the most scientific because the child has recognized that rolling down a slope is an example of the more general idea of moving downwards under the influence of a pulling force. The big ideas of science – in this case, gravity – have this quality of greater general application and ability to provide explanations for events. However, all three statements are 'ideas' in the sense of being opinions about why something has happened.

While teachers were sometimes concerned that some children appeared to have few ideas, they also sometimes encountered the complete opposite. A few children, particularly younger ones, seemed to have too many ideas, volunteering a stream of opinions without showing a particular commitment to any of them. Having ideas became an exercise in fantasy or imagination.

While fantasy goes beyond scientific endeavour, imagination does not. Children should not be discouraged from having ideas. But they must gradually become aware of the need to test those ideas critically. This is a necessity in science. Where ideas are so fantastic that there is no way they can be tested, they need not be dismissed; but at the same time they have to be recognized as being outside science.

Finding out children's ideas

What can I do to encourage children to express ideas?

The teacher who wants to start from children's ideas needs to know what the children are really thinking, not what they think they are expected to say. Any judgement of a child's current understanding is an assessment of his or her thinking. But we can't have direct access to children's thoughts; they must be invited and helped to express what they are thinking.

Both the nature and the context of this invitation are important in giving the child confidence to reveal his or her thoughts. Children should be given time to observe and explore real objects. This arouses interest and focuses attention so that the children are really 'tuned in' to the events involved. They have time to think and to ask themselves questions about what they have noticed. Your questions will thus appear more natural than if they come out of the blue.

Those questions need to be phrased to allow varying responses. In this 'finding out' role the teacher is a listener, encouraging children to put forward ideas and probing for further clarification where necessary.

Your attitude is crucial. You must encourage the expression of these ideas and treat them with respect as the child's starting point. If you immediately offer a more scientifically acceptable alternative to supplant those ideas, children will quickly realize that their views are not being taken seriously. It is the child who must discover whether his or her ideas will stand up to new experiences, investigations and other people's opinions.

We outline in this chapter several techniques that SPACE project teachers have used to draw out children's ideas. They are:

◆ open questioning;
◆ whole class discussion;
◆ children-only group discussion;
◆ annotated drawings and diagrams (including comic strip drawings);
◆ writing (including class log books).

What is meant by open questioning?

Questions need to be worded in such a way that children feel free to express their own ideas. Such questions are open, in that they have no preconceived, single, correct answer. (In practice, the degree of open-endedness in a question is determined by the preceding dialogue.) Some examples from trials of the SPACE approach are:

'What do you think makes it stop?'
'Can you tell me a bit more about that?'
'What could you do to make it quieter?'
'What do you think is happening inside the eggs?'

When asking children to express their ideas, certain approaches are often useful.

◆ Try to formulate questions from the actual wording used by children. Accepting the language used by children helps them recognize that their ideas are respected and valued. This in turn gives them the confidence to say more and to explain their ideas further.

◆ Non-verbal responses, particularly facial expression, should be carefully controlled. 'That's an interesting idea; how could you test it out?', delivered with an encouraging look, is the most productive kind of reaction.

◆ Give children time to formulate their answers to these open questions. The normal response of a teacher to two seconds or so of silence following a question is likely to be to ask another question or to take some other similar supportive action. However, it would be much more helpful to extend this waiting time deliberately to eight to ten seconds. Once children have accepted that you will wait for an answer, more thoughtful and articulate answers become possible. There will be far fewer 'don't know' replies. But if the teacher doesn't wait, children learn that the answer will eventually come from the teacher and so they won't bother to think.

How can I make the best use of whole class discussion?

Whole class discussion is a commonly used technique, particularly when starting a topic or rounding one off. In such discussions teachers frequently do most of the talking. Typically, children address all their comments to the teacher. If the aim is to find out children's ideas, you have to be far more of a listener.

The starting point will need to be an open question about some experience that children have shared. Children will need encouragement to respond to each other's remarks as well as to yours. Choose your own remarks to guide the discussion, as unobtrusively as possible, so that each child:

◆ knows that the question under discussion is genuinely open;
◆ feels secure in expressing his or her ideas because they will be taken seriously;
◆ has ample opportunity and time to express ideas;
◆ acknowledges the value of ideas put forward by others;
◆ is prepared to offer and to receive comments in a constructive way.

Children's involvement in formulating their ideas, attempting to communicate them and listening to alternative explanations by their peers is a valuable learning process. It will make them more aware of the role of debate and inquiry in science.

How can children-only group discussions be useful?

In any class there are children who, in spite of our best attempts, find it extremely difficult to contribute to discussions held in large groups. Using groups of only four to six can help here. Furthermore, groups of this size give all children an opportunity to share in the thinking of their peers in much greater detail. They can also concentrate more on issues that they think are important.

Here is a short extract taken from one such discussion.

Denise: When you hit it, the sound sort of vibrates around the drum and at the bottom it comes out.

Chris: The sound travels around the air until it gets to you.

Denise: When you beat it, the sound vibrates, and if you hit it heavy it makes a loud vibrating sound. The vibration travels to your ear to the brain.

Ashley: The sound runs down to the bottom and goes back up and through to the top to the ear. The sound runs from the ear to the brain and tells you that a drum is making a noise.

Chris: The vibrations send out sounds which our ear picks up.

Sonia: I think when we beat the drum, the sound echoed to the bottom and then comes out and makes a sound. It goes to the bottom, it bounces off the bottom, echoes back up and makes a booming sound.

John: No, the thin material is tight to give the echoey sound. The materials is so thin that when you hit the drum the noise goes into the wooden bit at the bottom and echoes.

It is doubtful whether a teacher-managed discussion could have been so effective in bringing out these idiosyncratic understandings.

Obviously it is not possible to listen in to several small group discussions simultaneously. But it may be possible to tape them and listen to them later.

Just listening to one or two such discussions will reveal some of the ideas that are held. Alternatively, children may report on their discussions. Again they should be aware that the intention is not necessarily for them to reach a group conclusion but rather to present their ideas, whether similar or different.

It is undoubtedly true that both small group and whole class discussion will cause shifts in some children's thinking as they influence each other. It should be remembered that merely trying to find out a child's ideas will affect these to some extent, clarifying or even changing them. In either case this gives a basis for further work.

Children may need time to become used to working in groups. First attempts are often not successful, particularly with children accustomed to classrooms where discussion is not encouraged. Building up confidence and effectiveness in group discussion is important, not only in science.

Discussions can be planned as part of English speaking and listening activities, so you may be able to spend more time on them and not treat them as an additional activity.

Can children's ideas be found from their annotated drawings?

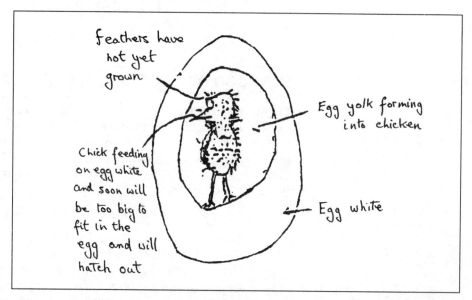

The answer to this question is a definite 'yes' as long as the children are asked to express in their drawings what their ideas are and not just to represent what can be seen. Often their drawing ability is not up to expressing their ideas, and this is where annotation comes in. Annotated drawings and diagrams were succinctly described by one very young SPACE project contributor as 'pictures with words on'. They can provide particularly useful insights into children's thinking, because:

◆ they make relatively modest demands on teacher time in class;
◆ they do not require a one-to-one interaction;
◆ children do not have to be present when their drawings are assessed for the ideas they contain;
◆ they reveal the thinking of those who for one reason or another find expression through writing difficult (some of these children may need help with the annotation).

Talking to some children individually about their picture helps to clarify and to expand on some points they appear to have made in the drawing. 'Tell me about your picture' is one possible opening remark.

Children may not be used to mixing drawing and writing. At first they may be puzzled about what is being asked of them, and initial encouragement and guidance will be necessary. They need to be assured, for example, that their diagrams will not be judged for their artistic merit. Annotation does not have to consist of complete sentences. It is the expression of ideas that is important, and the annotated drawing should capture that.

Annotation expresses ideas that drawing alone cannot. For example, the writing on the drawing of the egg (see opposite) indicated that the unhatched chick could feed.

Annotated drawings can also show changes taking place. It is often revealing to ask for a series of diagrams arranged as a comic strip. In some cases change occurs too slowly to be perceptible. This example shows, in the form of a comic strip, one child's view of what happens during rusting.

The comic strip technique can also be used to explore children's predictions of change.

Can children's writing help to reveal their ideas?

If children can express themselves fairly fluently in writing, their responses to the teacher's open questions can be explored in this way. Ideally these questions will follow experience of real objects or events.

Here is the writing of one child who had seen a torch shine on a piece of paper.

> it pushes the air out the way and then
> when it gets on the card because the card
> is hard the light cant get through so it
> get stuck so you can see some light

This child has an idea of how light travels, but needs more experience and thought about what happens when it hits the card. The present explanation at least indicates that light can't go through it and would be useful in accounting for shadows. Clearly discovering children's thinking provides a basis for further work.

When long-term changes are being studied, teachers involved in SPACE research found it useful to establish a class log book. This was placed next to whatever was being investigated. It was used, for example, in studies of plant growth and of evaporation.

Children were encouraged to add their observations periodically during the relatively long time involved. Drawings could also be put in the log book instead of or as well as writing. Children could add their own ideas, with names and dates, when they felt they had something to say.

The class log book should be distinguished from an individual or class diary. Contributions are not demanded, but need to be encouraged. Like annotated drawings, log books give a basis for further discussion.

CHAPTER 9

Helping children to develop their ideas

How does the teacher start?

Having spent time finding out children's ideas, your role is then to use various techniques to encourage children to move their thinking along. Some teachers may find it difficult to switch from a technique which helps to find out existing ideas to one designed to develop understanding. It is important that you provisionally accept where children are in their thinking while looking for opportunities to help them develop those ideas.

To 'accept' an idea implies simply that one is realistic about children's starting points. Do not dismiss a child's position out of hand. Children's views often turn out to be carefully considered, and it is also well established that such ideas may be held with a conviction that is hard to shift.

How can children's ideas be built into investigations?

When children test their own ideas, the power of direct experience is coupled with the motivation arising from ownership of the ideas to be tested. The interplay between conceptual understanding and the use of process skills is crucially important in investigations.

Children may need help to restate their ideas so that they can be tested. Their first reaction may be to try to show that their ideas are right rather than to test them scientifically. Moreover, investigations are often conducted with little thought about whether the test is fair. Children might, for example, compare how well two makes of paper towel soak up water without ensuring that they use comparable pieces of the two makes or that they follow exactly the same procedures in the two tests.

On occasions, everyday notions of what is fair may conflict with what is fair in a scientific test. Children urged to make sure that a test is fair may simply ensure that everyone involved has a turn.

Accurate observations, accurate measurement and recording, care with the procedures used, interpretations that are consistent with the evidence, can all be discussed. Opportunities for such discussion should be provided by arranging for children to report on their investigations to other children and receive comments from them. The difference between recounting reactions to a film or a football match and reporting the outcomes of an investigation have to be learnt through experience and the guidance of the teacher.

What other ways are there to help children rethink their ideas?

Problem solving activities

Setting children practical problems which call on their knowledge and power to apply science ideas is well established as a classroom technique. The SPACE approach avoids the difficulties which can arise from dropping a problem on a group of children out of the blue. If you are using an integrated topic approach during which an opportunity for practical exploration arises, children can tackle the issue as a problem solving activity, starting with an understanding of the issue and some interest in pursuing it.

Some children, particularly girls, dislike problems that have no meaning or setting or wider relevance. The notion of a problem being of purely intrinsic interest works for some children but not for all. It will help most children if you can ensure that all science work is presented in a context that has a clear personal relevance to them, for it does seem that if this is not done children will sooner or later turn away from science.

Social exchange of ideas

While direct experience is the touchstone for learning in the primary school, it is also true that many ideas are acquired, modified and developed during social interactions. Reporting ideas carries with it the discipline of putting together and expressing notions which may be barely formed. Justifying an interpretation to others requires that the evidence be made at least to appear as carefully weighed and judged. In a discussion there may be opposing points of view, expressed and supported by differing interpretations of the evidence. Your role is to convene such discussions, ensure fair play, and ensure that children actually listen to each other's views.

Representations of ideas

When children first make their drawings they will probably pay little attention to the representation they use. You should try to make this a more self-conscious exercise, perhaps by encouraging children to compare their drawings with the attempts of other children and to discuss the differences. Drawings, like spoken language, communicate understanding; some representations work well, perhaps because they use an imagery that communicates ideas powerfully and economically. Thus drawings are not just a second-best method for those who cannot write prose; they can enrich the development and sharing of understanding in a unique way.

In the topic of 'Sound', for example, representations are essential because sound is invisible.

The first two drawings show ways of representing sound often used in comics. However, neither corresponds to any testable idea about how

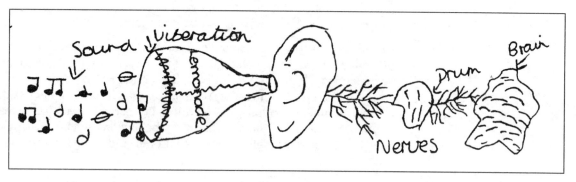

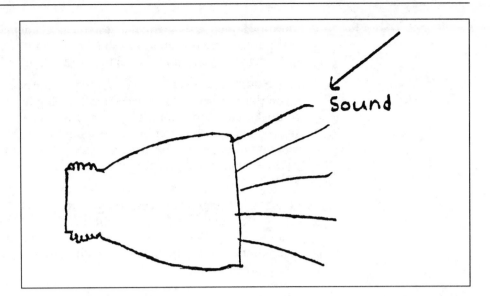

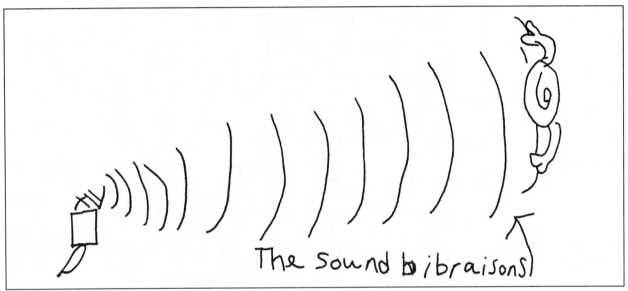

sound travels. In contrast, the second two drawings show lines coming from the source and directions of travel, and arcs which could be thought of as respresenting areas of high and low pressure spreading out from the source. Thus, a change from the first two drawings to the third to the fourth drawings would be evidence of progression towards more scientific ideas about how sound travels.

Generalizations

Throughout childhood, conceptual development evolves through the accumulation of experiences. Exposure to one specific instance of a science idea is only a beginning; generalization from the first specific context to a wider range of examples is essential. Activities in the Nuffield Primary Science materials will help to start this process, and it is important that it be supported by calling on examples beyond those explored in the classroom. Children's ability to relate classroom experiences to the outside world often arises from class discussion. For example, children who were exploring evaporation discussed what had happened to the clothes they had washed, and then were asked to think of other instances. Suggestions included a kettle boiling dry; drops of water in a paddling pool; paint drying on a palette. Incorrect generalizations were also proposed: milk disappearing into cereals and water into plants. These ideas showed that children were confusing evaporation with absorption, the link being the 'disappearance' of the water. These incorrect generalizations can give the teacher valuable information about the child's current level of understanding, and pointers as to how learning might proceed.

Many SPACE teachers have commented on the ease with which children given the opportunity can associate learning in the classroom with other contexts. This contrasts with reports from secondary education which suggest that children tend to keep school learning about science quite separate from personally acquired views about how the world works. It could be that the SPACE approach can help to avoid this kind of split.

Generalization provides useful information for assessment. Problems in new contexts cannot be tackled by factual recall alone, so a child can show understanding in applying a learnt idea in a new way. Indeed, the gradual accumulation of experience in using an idea enables children to identify and extract its critical attributes, leading to a higher order of conceptual development.

Extending children's experience

Young children are strongly influenced by what they can perceive directly. However, many of the things we try to understand in science are not directly observable. Energy is observable only in its effects. We cannot see gravity or sound. Other phenomena are imperceptible because they are outside the human scale. For example, we cannot see evaporation of a liquid, or plant or animal growth, actually taking place. Is there any way in which we can make such phenomena accessible to children?

In the case of evaporation, we can sometimes sense that it is taking place, for example when we smell perfume. Admittedly, parallels with evaporation of water from a fish tank might not be obvious to children, and it might not help to take over the children's discussion and assert the similarity of the situations. However, the experience of 'smelling evaporation' could be set up as a thinking activity to start off new ideas in children's minds. Unless such a basis is laid, a demonstration lesson on the particle model of matter might fail to make contact with children's understanding.

Experience can also be extended through secondary sources such as books, videos and models. The Nuffield Primary Science pupils' books have a function here in providing information that children may use in mentally testing their ideas. The books also expose children to different ideas and ways of looking at things, promoting reflection and the need to justify their own ideas.

What if ideas cannot be investigated directly?

There are many aspects of the world that children cannot investigate or observe directly. Examples are the spherical shape of the Earth, the Earth's crust, the extinction of species and the interior of the human body.

It may sometimes be possible to go part way with investigation. Fossil remains may be looked at as evidence of past life forms, and observations in quarries, caves, or holes dug in the ground can be used to develop ideas about what is under the ground. However, secondary sources such as books, films and videotapes will have to be used to help children study some topics adequately.

Children have to make sense of ideas they find in such sources. It is important that they learn from them in an active way; that is, they should use them to seek evidence for their own ideas and questions. It is also to be hoped that they will seek to understand how the information was first established.

Sometimes secondary sources may usefully supplement first-hand exploration. When children explore the variety of living things, they should observe as many plants and animals as possible, but this experience can be widened vastly by use of other sources. The pupils' books will help here. Children's ideas will develop if they approach such sources with their own questions. For example, having seen the way that some animals look after their young, they might want to find what other animals do.

How can we help children towards a better understanding of the scientific terms they use?

It was clear in the SPACE research and development work that children sometimes used both technical and non-technical words in an idiosyncratic manner. They used the words scientists use to describe events, but often without the meaning that scientists attach to them.

Activities which encourage children to think carefully about what they understand by particular words should be devised to:

◆ clarify the meanings and usage of words in the children's everyday vocabulary;
◆ consider alternative words that children use for a certain thing, so that the nuances of related words, in both scientific and everyday vocabulary, may be drawn out;
◆ help children to use more accurately the scientific terms that emerged as they tried to describe their science activities. (Scientific vocabulary was introduced only when children had evidently identified an idea or process for which they lacked a precise label.)

For example, children frequently used the words 'rough' and 'smooth' in connection with the surfaces on which toy cars were propelled. Comparisons were made between different surfaces, for example the playground surface and the floor of the hall. The children made rubbings of rough and smooth surfaces. They collected objects and sorted them into rough and smooth groups. These groups exemplified particular words and enabled the children to use the words more accurately and in a relevant context.

A useful strategy for developing understanding, particularly amongst infants, was thinking of other contexts in which the word was used. One teacher asked children to think of instances where they had heard the words 'melt' and 'wet' used.

> Candles melt on a cake.
>
> Chocolate melts in your hand.
>
> A towel dries you when you are wet.
>
> Wet clothes dry.
>
> Wet paint dries on paper.

These suggestions were turned into activities, after which children drew pictures of their observations and discussed the outcomes. This let children distinguish between what had 'melted' and what was simply 'wet'. By this method the everyday haphazard acquisition of word meanings was subjected to some control. The two essential aspects were:

◆ shared and unambiguous direct experience through which every child involved was able to agree the characteristics of the phenomenon;
◆ shared use and discussion of particular vocabulary. If we are to communicate effectively, we have to make considerable efforts to establish conventional meanings.

How should children be introduced to scientific vocabulary?

The experience of teachers involved in the SPACE project has been that merely supplying a child with a scientific label has not helped understanding. Children have either not used the technical term because they did not know enough, or have used it inappropriately.

On the other hand, children use alternatives to the technical terms with which they are completely satisfied and which work perfectly satisfactorily for their level of understanding. These alternatives have been constructed and refined from previous experiences, so children are likely to find them much more helpful in expressing their ideas. We need to value the words children use to describe their ideas as well as the ideas themselves. The major task in language development in this context is to judge accurately the point at which the children themselves feel the need for new words.

The words children used as synonyms sometimes revealed a lot about their understanding of a concept. While working on the 'Growth' topic, a significant number of children used the word 'stretch' as an alternative to the word 'grow'. In an attempt to clarify children's understanding of these words, a Year 3 teacher listened to children's suggestions of objects that would illustrate the ideas – a spring, a balloon filled with water, treacle toffee and knitting – and provided them for examination.

> The children's notion of 'grow' and 'stretch' became increasingly confused as these objects challenged their understanding. A consensus view seemed to be that growth was a permanent state whereas stretch would go back. There was also a belief that growth involved adding on to, like building a wall or knitting.

Careful exploration of the words children use may reveal underlying ideas about what is happening which are strange or even confused. Direct experiences, discussion and drawing can have some impact on children's understanding of the words they use, but it has to be recognized that linguistic development is a gradual process enhanced by encountering a range of different experiences. As one teacher said:

> Many children will need reinforcement activities over months and years to develop their understanding.

Assessment and record keeping

How does assessment fit into the SPACE approach?

Collecting and using information about children's ideas and skills is an essential part of the SPACE approach to teaching and learning. It could be said that knowing about children's starting points is important for any teaching, for only then is there any chance of providing experiences that build on what a child can already do and understand.

Assessment of change in children's ideas automatically follows from the regular gathering of information to establish children's ideas at any particular time. Finding out what children understand about a topic is a necessary first step in choosing suitable activities; finding out what they understand after the activities not only indicates what changes have taken place, but also gives a starting point for further work.

If these regular looks at children's ideas were to be carried out through any formal methods of assessment, such as tests, it would waste time and lose the thread of the investigation. Therefore it is important that such assessment should be an integral part of the activities. You should constantly seek to gather information which helps you to understand a child's thinking. This could be by listening, watching, open questioning or studying what has been produced. For instance while discussing with a child how she thought a paper dart could be made to stay in the air for longer, a teacher was able to discover this girl's ideas about why things fall.

This informality must not be taken to imply lack of rigour. In fact, the more informal the methods of assessment, the more attention must be given to ensuring that at some point in their activities information is gathered about each one of the children in relation to all the aspects of their learning. Planning and records of the accumulating information are obviously essential.

When planning for assessment, it is useful to consider the whole context of activity planning.

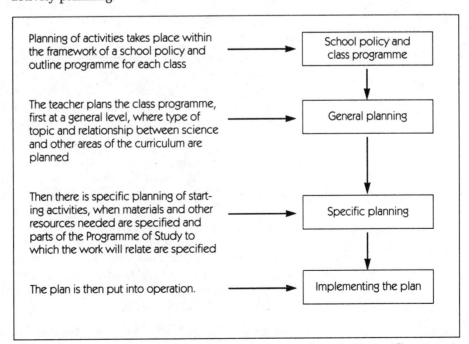

Planning of activities takes place within the framework of a school policy and outline programme for each class → School policy and class programme

The teacher plans the class programme, first at a general level, where type of topic and relationship between science and other areas of the curriculum are planned → General planning

Then there is specific planning of starting activities, when materials and other resources needed are specified and parts of the Programme of Study to which the work will relate are specified → Specific planning

The plan is then put into operation. → Implementing the plan

Deciding how to gather information about children's ideas, and considering how this information might be used, especially in planning further activities, are important elements of the SPACE approach.

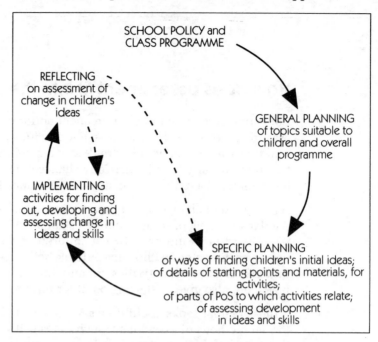

Assessment of initial ideas and of any change in them is shown here as part of both planning and implementation. It is not an afterthought and does not require different activities.

How does assessment in the SPACE approach fit in with the National Curriculum assessment?

In any assessment the information gathered about what a child can do or understand is compared with some expectation or standard. This is true of informal assessment as much as of formal testing. In informal assessment the standard or 'expectation' may be one for that particular child; the same behaviour from another child might be judged differently. This is quite acceptable when the purpose is to provide feedback to the children about their own individual progress. However, if information is to be more widely applicable, the same standards or expectations should be applied to all the children.

In the National Curriculum, the level descriptions provide the common bases, or criteria, for assessing children's progress. They indicate certain levels in the development of children's ideas and skills. They are useful not only in arriving at the occasional summary of achievement but in tracing progress from one level to another.

Level descriptions are broad and encompass all the achievement relating to each Attainment Target. It is necessary to look across a range of children's work to find evidence of the ideas and skills that match a particular level. It is helpful in this process to have an idea of what characterizes work at a certain level. Work in a variety of topics and contexts can then be assessed and not just work closely related to specific statements in the descriptions. Teachers have to be able to translate the general idea of a level into the topic of the children's work. In the chapters on assessment in the Nuffield Primary Science teachers' guides there are indications of what to look for in children's work in the context of the guide topic, as indications of achievement at certain levels.

Working with the Nuffield Primary Science teachers' guides, you will be assessing the children's ideas and skills at the start of the topic and then gathering information later in the activities. This provides all the information necessary for applying the National Curriculum criteria. All that is needed further, at times when a summary of achievement is required, is to express this information in terms of National Curriculum levels. Each teachers' guide has a chapter designed to help with this. It provides commentaries on examples of children's work which help to show how the general principles apply in specific cases. These chapters emphasize that the kind of activities described in the guides provide all the evidence needed without giving the children special tasks or tests.

In practice, of course, the work of many children will not seem to fit neatly into levels. The process of assessment is not streamlined and neat; children sometimes seem to have developed a skill or idea but later behave as if they hadn't.

An important thought to keep in mind is the purpose of the assessment, which is not to be able to label children as being able to do this or that but to help their learning through finding out about their skills and ideas.

What techniques are there for assessing children's ideas and process skills?

It is useful to think in terms of *sources of* information and then of *how* information is gathered from these sources.

There are really only two sources of information for the assessment we are concerned with:

◆ children's actions: what they do or say;
◆ children's products: what they write, draw, make or set up.

The important difference between these sources is the permanence of the information they provide. This feature is significant because it relates to the time the teacher has for considering and reconsidering what the child has done. It has implications for planning to collect relevant information from all children in a class. Clearly what children do or say is not permanently recorded (unless it is taped, which is unlikely to be routine), and so this information has to be used in making an assessment on the spot. It is unlikely that this can be done for more than a few children at any one time. But a drawing, say, can be stored, examined, compared with others made by the child, and discussed with people who were not there when it was created. Moreover, the products of many children can be considered.

Before we turn to how information can be gathered from these sources, it should perhaps be made clear that ideas are not necessarily assessed from products, nor skills assessed from actions, even though this is a tempting association to make. Both products and actions can be used in assessing both children's ideas and their process skills. Where possible both sources should be used, for either source alone may be insufficient. For example, it is not always possible to be sure from what children do whether their action had the purpose we might ascribe to it, but this can sometimes be clear from a written account or an end product. Similarly, what children mean in their drawing or writing is not always clear, and it is helpful to discuss it with them and possibly to annotate the product for later reference (see Chapter 8).

For example, this description of results of an investigation with a string telephone has ambiguities in it, but also reveals ample potential for skills and ideas to be assessed:

> We went into the corridor and took the beaker telephone with us. We held the beaker tightly and we spoke into the beaker and we could hear very clearly and when we bent we could not hear properly.

There would seem to be some information about the child's ability to use investigative skills, in particular to use observations to support conclusions and compare what was observed with what was expected. However, it is not clear what 'we bent' means (round a corner or just letting the string go slack?), or whether other factors were kept the same when 'bending' was tried. If a teacher observed the investigation, or discussed it with the child afterwards, this point would be cleared up. There would also be information about whether the child had suggested questions that could be tested, had recognized the need for a 'fair' test, or knew that sound can travel through different materials.

We have a reminder here of the importance of being prepared, of planning to gather information for assessment, and of having in mind the criteria to be applied in making judgements. In this way opportunities to gather information are not missed.

How can practical work be assessed?

Much of the information for assessing children's practical work has to be collected by observation and needs on-the-spot judgements. This is particularly important for young children, whose products are unlikely to convey the full story of their interaction with materials.

For example, a class of middle infants was studying seeds. The children and their teacher had collected many different kinds, from fruits they had eaten, from trees and hedgerows, from their kitchen shelves and from seed packets. These formed a daily increasing display in the classroom. Groups had been working at various times on sorting and comparing the seeds, measuring them, making patterns with them, planting them in various conditions and carefully opening them to look inside.

The parts of the Programme of Study for Key Stage 1 to which these activities related were:

That pupils should be taught:

- to explore using appropriate senses;
- to make observations and measurements;
- to communicate what happens during their work;
- to make simple comparisons;
- to use results to draw conclusions;
- to indicate whether the evidence collected supports any prediction made;
- to try to explain what they found out, drawing on their knowledge and understanding. (Sc1)

and ...

- that plants need light and water to grow;
- that flowering plants grow and produce seeds which, in turn, produce new plants;
- that living things can be grouped according to observable similarities and differences. (Sc2)

Each session with the seeds lasted no more than half an hour, so there was no time to gather information about all the children. The teacher selected five children as the foci of observation in any one session. These children were unaware of being chosen, and the teacher interacted normally with all the children while making notes about the 'target' five. He was guided in making these observations by a list of questions for which he sought answers from each of the five:

Did the child:

make at least one relevant observation (e.g. find a way in which seeds were different)?

ask questions and suggest ideas (e.g. about why some seeds are bigger than others, have different colours, etc.)?

make related observations (e.g. about the size of the seedlings in relation to the size of the seed)?

make an interpretation based on the observation or investigation (e.g. that water was needed to make the seeds grow)?

know that the seeds were part of living things?

know that the seeds needed certain things to remain alive?

know that the seeds would grow into plants of the kind which produced them?

realize that certain plants grow in certain places and that some seeds (e.g. spices) do not normally grow in this country?

treat the seeds and seedlings with appropriate care?

These questions relate very closely to part of the level descriptions for Sc1 and Sc2 (for levels 1 and 2, although the list of questions could be extended to include relevant aspects of level 3). Some of the questions could be answered by observation, but others depended on discussion with children. In these discussions the teacher framed more open questions which would give more information about the children's ideas, for example:

◆ What differences do you notice between these seeds?
◆ Where do you think these seeds came from? How do you think they were created?
◆ [If the children think they are alive] How can we keep them alive and make sure they don't die?
◆ What do you think these will grow into?

This information was gathered as part of the teacher's regular teaching; that is, between visits to other groups, where he may well have asked similar questions. He did not, however, attempt to overload his memory by trying to recall all the responses and check systematically on all the children except for the five targets. The only difference in his behaviour in respect of the five targets was in his deliberate attempt to take in information while interacting normally. He did not stand over them with a checklist or ignore children from other groups who needed his help.

Having gathered as much as possible of this information about these five children, the teacher would record the significant points immediately after the session, perhaps noting for his own use the evidence on which he decided whether the child did or did not do what was expressed in the question.

In later sessions other children would be selected as targets for observation. In the case of the assessment relating to Sc1 it would not matter if the observations were made when children were working on investigations of things other than seeds, which is why these questions were expressed above in general terms followed by 'translations' into the seeds context in parentheses. Over the year the teacher would observe all the children in detail in several different activities and so would be able to judge the extent to which skills were being used generally.

For the Sc2 assessment, clearly the subject matter has to be living things and so information has to be gathered only when the children are working on this subject. Much of the information for the Sc2 assessment could come from the discussion described on page 61; or from examples of the children's writing and drawings done during the activities.

How do I keep track of children's activities?

Teachers keep records in different degrees of detail for different purposes. Now proper records have to be kept in all areas, giving many teachers more work than in the past. The real danger of overload is an important factor in deciding on a recording system, for there is no one way of keeping records. Other factors are the preferences of individual teachers and what they are required to do in order to keep records compatible with what has been decided for the whole school for, if this is not done, the value of records as a means of communication is lessened. For these reasons we do not propose a specific form of record but offer some suggestions which may be taken into account in choosing or designing recording procedures and forms.

One type is a record of planned activities. The following example includes not only the activities to be undertaken by the children and the parts of the KS2 Programmes of Study covered but also, through the identification of key questions, planning for the information to be gathered for assessment.

General topic:	Time			
Date	Specific activity	Part of Programme of Study	Key ideas/skills	Key questions
Wb 15/1	Sundials	Sc1 Investigation Sc4 – Track path of Sun using safe procedure – learn about motion of Earth – investigate formation of shadows.	Predicting Careful observations and measurements. Daily movement of Sun. Rotation of Earth about axis. Shadow formed where light cannot pass through.	What will happen to shadow? Ask for explanation of why shadow is formed; why Sun appears to move.

This has important uses, particularly if it is updated after the event by adding things that happened but were unplanned and deleting those that did not happen. Depending on the organization of teaching, a column could be added to indicate which children were involved in each activity. The information about what actually took place is input into planning of subsequent activities.

How can I record progress in learning usefully and efficiently?

It is important to distinguish between a record of activities and a record of achievement. Keeping an account of information about what children have achieved in terms of ideas and skills (and other attributes, such as attitudes, if desired) is important not only for deciding later experiences for children but for meeting the requirements of continuous assessment (teacher assessment) for the National Curriculum.

If teachers are not to be overwhelmed by the work of keeping records the process has to be kept in bounds, unnecessary detail avoided and transcribing from one form to another avoided or reduced to a minimum. Guidelines from your school or LEA would be helpful here.

A relatively simple way to record children's achievement is to note it on the planning chart in an additional column. Over the course of the plan it should be possible to note the significant points of achievement for each child. If required by the school, this information can be built into detailed individual records. It could also form a basis for making more formal judgements supported by evidence in the form of a limited number of examples of children's work.

Equal opportunities

Does the SPACE approach provide science for all pupils?

An approach which starts where the children are should appeal to both boys and girls and those of all cultural backgrounds. As far as possible, children with special educational needs should have the same science experience as others.

The Nuffield Primary Science materials have been developed with this firmly in mind. Indeed, since the SPACE approach to teaching and learning is designed to encourage each child to build on and develop her or his own skills, it can be used successfully across a very wide range of levels of development. The relationship between the ideas children have and the way these are developing means that children are operating at different levels within the same curriculum. Children with difficulties do not become isolated by their differences.

Ensuring equal opportunities for learning includes avoiding unconscious discrimination. There are three main sources of inequality; in examining them we will look at the circumstances that are associated with bias, how to avoid them, and how the SPACE approach helps.

What can be done to avoid gender-related bias?

It has been well documented that there are gender differences in participation and performance in science. These differences appear in all western countries, where they have been studied mainly at the secondary level. Yet the problem clearly has its roots at primary level, and the APU findings showed that trends for boys to perform better in physical science were already evident at the end of primary school. It is not uncommon in primary schools for girls' participation in activities more often to take the form of watching or writing and for boys to be dominating the 'doing'.

Several hypotheses have been put forward to account for these differences; they fall into two groups: biological and social. The biological have included a traditional idea that females were constitutionally unsuited to science, and the more recent theory of sex differences in visual-spatial ability. However, there is overwhelming evidence (particularly from non-western countries) that there is no inherent sex difference in related skills.

The SPACE approach helps children to choose from their own ideas in trying to understand what they find, to test their ideas and to take part in the 'human construction' of knowledge. This is in itself likely to reduce gender bias. However, children are influenced by their out-of-school experiences, so teachers still need to see that girls are encouraged to participate equally with boys in all activities. Only through experiencing science for themselves will girls overcome prejudices which are still fed by social pressures and the media.

It is also important to take into account the differences in interests of girls and boys. The origin of these, in cultural expectations, in role models in the home and the media, in gender-differentiated toys and so on, have generally been very effective in producing distinct sets of gender-related interests from an early age. Although these different interests affect all areas of the curriculum, they have particular relevance to science. Boys' tendency towards things mechanical often attracts them to activities relating to forces, electricity and magnetism, and energy (Sc4). Girls' interests tend to take them away from mechanical things and towards activities relating to living things (Sc2). A special effort is needed to engage both sexes in these areas particularly. Otherwise the lack of experience will lead to lower performance which itself creates dislike of things 'I'm no good at', and eventually to under-representation of boys in biology and girls in physical science.

Can the SPACE approach help to avoid bias relating to cultural background?

Just as pupils can feel excluded if the subject of activities does not interest them, so they can experience the same reaction if it bears no relation to their cultural experience. This problem is curriculum-wide and calls for sensitivity. The purpose of an activity may be entirely missed or engagement may be resented if inappropriate assumptions are made. This happened when a six-year-old was making a reindeer, as were all her classmates, just before Christmas. All the others were going to take theirs home to hang on their tree, but this little girl was Jewish. She worked very reluctantly. In science, cultural background may not be thought to be a problem, because science is about the world we all live in. But daily experiences, from which so many science activities start, may be quite different for children with a family background and a tradition in other countries. An obvious example is the discussion of food. If this deals exclusively with English fare, pupils of other ethnic origins may be unable to relate this to their own daily lives, and may feel that science does not concern them.

Not only content but the way pupils are encouraged to behave in science – touching, questioning, challenging – may distance certain children. It may take considerable persuasion to prise out ideas from children who expect the teacher to be the source of all ideas. Often this is compounded by gender and the way girls are expected to behave.

The use of children's ideas may have to be introduced carefully to children who find it unnatural to put forward any ideas that do not derive from some authority, such as a book or the teacher. It is often best to include these children in groups where other children's ideas are freely given and used. This legitimates the expression of their own ideas more effectively than compelling them to say something before they realize why this is useful. Success here is the essential step in avoiding cultural bias. When children express their ideas and work on them and discuss their experiences, they are unlikely to be or feel excluded.

How does the SPACE approach help children with learning difficulties?

Often children who experience difficulties in areas where lack of language skills holds them back show unexpected understanding in science. But there will also be children who experience difficulties in science. Children with sensory disorders may have trouble making observations. Collecting objects and making measurements may pose problems for physically handicapped youngsters. Some children may have difficulty articulating their ideas because of communication disorders or lack of confidence. Children may also have difficulty in developing investigations, working co-operatively, or drawing conclusions from their observations.

Children who have experienced difficulties in the classroom are often regarded as unresponsive, reticent or simply lacking in ideas. An aim of the SPACE approach is for children to express their ideas confidently. This can only be achieved by creating an atmosphere in which children are willing to say what they think. There are several ways to do this.

An initial activity which takes account of children's own experience and allows them to explore real objects within their own capabilities is crucial. This direct experience provokes thought and may reveal hidden depths of understanding. Providing such opportunities for all children, including those with sensory disorders and communication difficulties, is the first step in participating in scientific activity.

Use of diverse techniques for expressing ideas allows children to communicate, independent of individual abilities. Some children may discuss their ideas more willingly on a one-to-one basis while others may be more responsive in small groups. Allowing children to represent their ideas in drawings, which can be annotated by the teacher, ensures that children with writing or communication difficulties can express their ideas. Offering different ways in which ideas can be expressed makes all techniques of equal value, so that participation in science does not depend on possessing specific skills.

Since children's own ideas form the basis of future activities, the SPACE approach ensures that learning activities are closely matched to a child's own abilities. All children have the opportunity to complete a purposeful task and to experience success. This positive outcome benefits children's confidence and motivation. Teachers have reported that when children's interest in a topic is reinforced, they spend more time on tasks and are less likely to become distracted.

Catering for children's individual abilities does not mean providing a whole range of different practical activities, let alone one for each child. Children can engage in an activity at several levels. Starting with their ideas allows each to make an individual response within the same activity.

Nor is catering for individuals incompatible with promoting co-operative learning – quite the opposite. An infants' teacher reported how a child, David, with severe communication difficulties, expressed and explored his ideas about floating and sinking. He made a boat with a bridge that held the front and the back sections together. He was convinced it would float, even when the other children suggested it might sink because of the gap between back and front sections. David himself went on to test his boat and was pleased when he proved it would float. Another child offered an explanation, claiming that it floated because it was 'more even'. This led another child to begin generating theories about why the boat floated and a co-operative attempt to find the best explanation resulted. During the development work for the Nuffield Primary Science materials it was clear that children began to recognize the contribution of their less able peers as valuable, and included these formerly less popular children in their investigations. The result was increased self-esteem, which may transfer to other learning and social situations.

Teachers using the SPACE approach have indicated a number of ways in which the needs of children who experience difficulties in science can be addressed.

- ◆ Emphasis on direct experience challenges children's thinking and understanding while placing learning in a meaningful and purposeful context.
- ◆ Valuing and responding to children's ideas will increase confidence and willingness to express ideas.
- ◆ Providing diverse ways of expressing ideas allows all to become involved.
- ◆ Using various methods of working from children's ideas leads to the experience of success, which creates enthusiasm for science.

The role of process skills

What are the process skills of science?

Science process skills are what we use when we make sense of information about the world. Scientists use these skills in advancing knowledge of how and why things work; children use them in developing understanding of events and phenomena they encounter in their rapidly expanding experience; anyone could use them in deepening their understanding throughout life.

It is helpful to identify separate process skills, although in practice several are generally used at once.

Observing

Gathering information by using the senses; may result in identifying similarities and differences, noticing details and sequence, ordering events.

Measuring

Being able to say 'how much' by comparing with some unit. This might be by reference to a non-standard unit such as a handspan but, with experience, it would increasingly involve using standard units (centimetres) and suitable measuring instruments (rulers).

Hypothesizing

Suggesting reasons for events or phenomena that can be tested scientifically; involves applying concepts and ideas from previous experience.

Predicting

Proposing what will happen, or what may be found, in the future, on the basis of evidence or experience.

Planning and carrying out investigations

Identifying how to find something out through practical manipulation of materials, recognizing the factors to be controlled and changed, how measurements are to be made and how results are to be collected and recorded; carrying this out in practice.

Interpreting

Putting information together by identifying patterns or trends and relationships between one variable and another.

Inferring

Drawing tentative conclusions from results of an investigation or from information collected.

Communicating

Presenting information or an account of events in such a way as to be understood by an audience; may involve use of diagrams, charts, tables, graphs and models.

It is fair to ask what makes these processes 'scientific'; don't we all make observations, hypotheses, predictions and inferences every day? We do, but not always with the rigour characteristic of science. Words such as 'predict' are used in a non-scientific context with much looser meaning. 'I predict she will have a great future' is not meant as a prediction for testing a particular hypothesis. 'I observe that you have been late too many times' is a judgement and not information gained through the senses. 'What's your hypothesis?' often means 'What's your guess?' Here there is no intention to treat the subject systematically or rigorously. Such treatment is that hallmark of scientific activity and distinguishes between scientific and everyday processes.

What role do process skills have in children's learning?

Children use process skills in making sense of new experiences, as we have just suggested. When used with scientific rigour the result is greater understanding. New experience is linked to existing ideas through the children's own observation, hypothesizing, investigation and so on. Sometimes the initial idea is challenged by new experience and has to be modified, or even abandoned for an idea that fits the evidence better. As a result the children's ideas become more widely applicable and so more useful in understanding the world. The word 'understanding' is important here, since we are concerned with the development of concepts that children regard as their own, ones they have worked out and which make sense to them. These will be used in trying to understand further experiences.

We should remember, however, that the way we use process skills depends on our knowledge of the phenomenon or object we are investigating. For example, in observing a patch of meadow, we might pick out some features or patterns that we think important; but a botanist, drawing on greater knowledge of plants, will observe many patterns that we would not notice. Similarly, if you do not know that light affects plant growth, you would not control it in a test of other effects on plant growth, so that these tests, however well designed and carried out in other respects, would be worthless.

We can see the importance of these process skills in learning by considering what happens if we try to teach concepts without using them. If we try to tell children that, for example, sound can travel through different materials without enabling them to observe or test out this idea, their only recourse is to rote learning. If the children believe, as many do, that sound passes from one place to another only through air and is stopped by solid materials, the new information is not only divorced from experience but conflicts with what they think happens. The children may memorize 'correct' ideas but still believe their own version, and they will be mystified by the difference. Little understanding results. Science becomes a series of meaningless rigmaroles; the subject quickly becomes disliked.

If instead the children test ideas, both their own and those they are given as alternatives, by making predictions and gathering evidence through observing, comparing and measuring to test these predictions, and are involved in deciding which idea fits the available evidence best, they have a chance of acquiring ideas that they know to 'work' and that make sense to them. This is learning with understanding.

It is clear that the way processes are carried out is crucial to whether ideas are properly tested. Children cannot immediately use the process skills described on page 67. Their abilities have to be developed so that their understanding can develop. As ideas become more sophisticated and abstract, the means of testing also need to become more precise, better focused and more consciously applied. Here we see the importance of helping children to develop their process skills, and the reason for emphasizing this in the SPACE approach to teaching science.

Progression in learning process skills

How do I recognize progression in process skills?

Observation and interpretations

In the course of the SPACE project work, teachers and researchers spent hundreds of hours listening to hundreds of children. Children's ideas and opinions were usually invited with the object of the discussion in full view: if discussion centred on plant or caterpillar or stick insect growth, a plant or insect would be there to see. This was to ensure that children had every possible support for the ideas they were trying to express; they could point and move things around to make their statements clear. It was noticeable, even with this contextual support, that they often ignored apparently obvious features.

The children's initial comments tended to be fairly low-level, and there weren't many of them. This is not to say that the children didn't have plenty to say. If they had raised a plant from seed they were proud to talk about it; children who had hatched chicks, or left a selection of materials outside to 'weather', showed tremendous involvement in the activities and wanted to talk about them. However, when the transcripts of these conversations were sieved for essential details, it appeared that the number of solid comments, even at the level of straightforward description, was less than expected. It was also clear that on average the number of comments increased with age, and that after more focused observation during further active investigation, the detail and number of observations which children made also increased. These are some of the signs of progress to look out for in children's observations.

From descriptions to explanations

Another kind of progression apparent in children's comments is the shift from the superficial to the more interpretative. This is seen as children become more familiar with a situation, and more frequently as children get older. It might be described as going beyond surface features and beginning to describe less visible underlying causes and mechanisms.

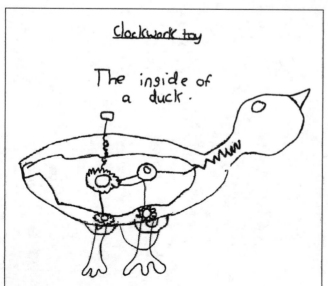

For many young children a sufficient account of the working of clockwork mechanisms was 'You turn the key and the wheels go round.' Only as they become drawn into the fascination of the mechanism, or more immediately if they are older, do they make attempts to fill in the gap between action and outcome. Initial attempts may be only fragmentary. Perhaps one component of the mechanism is described – a spring, a wheel, a cog – but without any clear links or sequences.

The train moves with the key. The key makes the wheels spin.

Sometimes a chain of causal reasoning may be stated in the reverse direction – infants may well assert that it gets dark because they go to bed. Or they may refer to supernatural agents. For them many events happen by magic, perhaps because such fantasies are generated and sustained by adults.

Expressing testable ideas

One kind of progress towards the generation of testable ideas, of which teachers taking part in the SPACE research were keenly aware, was in the reaction of children asked to make open-ended suggestions. Teachers found that these were at first regarded with suspicion, particularly by high-achieving children, who were the most reluctant to voice imaginative speculations. These children were used to success and expected this state of affairs to continue. They asked themselves, 'What is the right answer to the question?' and were confused to find there wasn't an expected right answer. Those children with lesser classroom reputations to protect were more likely to accept the spirit of the enquiry; they were not trapped in a history of being right. In time, of course, all the children came to understand more clearly that they were really meant to give their own ideas.

This kind of progress underpins the possibility of children testing their own ideas, and should not be taken for granted. Children must be helped to understand that they are invited and expected to express their ideas, however idiosyncratic. If only one class in a school is operating in this way, the teacher will not be able to assume the existence of these attitudes and skills.

When children begin to feel confident about expressing their ideas, they may be gently challenged to justify their assertions. Whenever possible, they should be encouraged to test their assertions in a rigorous manner. Then the conclusions they have drawn from their investigations should be reflected upon and discussed with other children. The teacher's role is to 'stand off' during the stage of the formulation and expression of hypotheses; but as children move on to testing them, their ideas have to hold up against a public set of rules.

What are the signs of progression in process skills?

There are several pointers to progression in scientific thinking and the use of scientific procedures. These procedures have to be learnt and are not acquired all at once. Examples of the changes which this learning entails are:

◆ Children have to learn how to express their ideas in a form that can be investigated. They must be aware which sorts of ideas can be investigated and which cannot.

◆ They have to learn to observe more carefully and thoroughly, so that they come to recognize regularities in the world around them and start to question how these happen.

◆ Once they have framed their question, children have to learn to see their thinking through. Typically, young children become fascinated by side issues and distracted from their initial intent.

◆ Children seem to have a natural inclination to view things (especially the actions of adults) as 'fair' or 'unfair'. They have to learn how to run a fair test of their idea. Many children's early activities are open attempts to confirm their assertion rather than to investigate a hypothesis.

◆ They should become more willing to use some form of quantification in their investigations. They may start with comparisons rather than measures.

◆ They should progress in their ability to translate a problem from a vague formulation (for example, 'Which is best?') to a form in which comparison or testing is made in terms of measurable quantities.

◆ Children also need to learn about, and to use effectively, an expanding range of measuring devices.

◆ There must be increasing organization in the collection and recording of information or data. From simple written keyword summaries they should gradually move to appropriate conventions such as tables, histograms, graphs, pie charts, etc.

◆ Once collected, information has to be displayed and interpreted. The kind of progression to expect might be from simple comparison ('This is the largest'), through expressing a general pattern in a vague way ('This goes with that'), then expressing patterns more precisely ('As this goes up, so does that'), and finally to describing more complex patterns.

◆ Gradually children need to become more objective, which for young children means being less egocentric, trying to see the evidence from someone else's point of view. The ability to reflect critically on their own plans and procedures may be found to lag slightly behind their capacity to express doubts about those of others.

Progression in learning ideas

How might I recognize progression?

Children's progress will not be limited to one facet of development. It will include progression:

◆ in skills
◆ in the formation of more abstract and more widely applicable ideas
◆ in the social skills that support practical investigations in groups.

If we are alert to the emerging signs of progress we are more likely to be in a position to encourage children's development.

Given the existence of the National Curriculum, one answer might be to take the Level Descriptions and see whether children have achieved the criteria for the next level. This might appear a rather limiting approach: limiting to teachers in the sense that there are many interesting opportunities to engage children in science activities which are likely to arise but which are not mentioned within the very broad Level Descriptions; limiting to children in the sense that there are many other subtle ways in which they may demonstrate progress; limiting most of all in the sense that such judgements would be 'all or nothing'. However, in thinking about children's progress, we must be absolutely clear that we are working in a time scale not of the time it takes to tell a fact, but of the time needed to understand an idea or acquire a skill. It may require days, weeks or years to build any depth of understanding.

When teachers are looking for signs of progression, it is absolutely crucial that their concerns should not stop at the products or levels achieved in tests. We are looking closely at the paths (there may be more than one) towards understanding of concepts. Teachers will be looking for opportunities to smooth or guide the course of development, to shape the outcomes.

The previous chapter considered signs of progress in the development of skills, and this chapter tries to show some of the more subtle indicators of progression in learning ideas.

What might indicate that children are making progress in learning ideas?

The reasoning of young children is often heavily dependent on direct sensory experiences or intuition. Therefore in looking for indications that children are making progress in their ideas we should look for evidence that they are moving towards the acceptance of more abstract ideas.

For example, when confronted with the fall in the water level in a tank, almost every child whose opinion was invited was willing and able to put forward an explanation of some sort. For some, the water had ceased to exist. (These are the children Piaget would have referred to as being pre-operational or non-conservers.) There is little doubt that this group was perceptually dominated: 'If I can't see it, it doesn't exist'. Another group of children offered very 'sensible' explanations as to the whereabouts of the water. If the water was no longer in the tank, somebody must have removed it. Prime suspect? The caretaker, of course! What is particularly interesting is the economy of the logic used; direct, like a short-circuit.

It is possible to see the signs of progress as children make the transition between a concrete interpretation of an event and a more abstract construction. In the case of evaporation of water, the abstract description is that particles of water too small to see leave the main body of water at a rate too slow to be perceptible, and take up position as an invisible gas (water vapour) dispersed in a transparent medium (air). One way that children might begin to show progress by showing their awareness of the various forms water takes in between being liquid and being invisible – mist, steam, spray, fog, droplets. Recognition of these perceptible forms indicates that the mechanism of evaporation of water may be more plausible to them, and in time they will feel comfortable with the idea of water assuming an invisible gaseous form. It is likely that many transitions to abstract models of how the world works are of this gradual and incomplete nature, rather than sudden revolutions in thinking.

Another way in which ideas progress from concrete to abstract is through the accumulation of experience. Familiarity with many instances of a class of objects – mammals, metals, conductors, flowering plants, or whatever – gradually enables us to abstract ('take from' them) their common property, their essential feature. We become able to distill mentally the essence of mammal, metal and so on. A child may notice rust on the precious shiny rims of her bicycle wheels; there may be rust on the school gate, on metal window frames, on a bridge. Only very gradually will a child build the notion of common properties within these very different and apparently unconnected contexts. More subtly, what do we make of the coins which were once so shiny having taken on a dull brown colour? And where do the rust-coloured cardigan and the autumn leaves that turn brown and disintegrate fit in this scheme?

Children show progress in the generalizing and discriminating more accurately. In time the accumulated wisdom of science offers higher-order generalizations. In time, children will learn (but not in the primary school) that all the examples of rusting have in common a reaction between the metal and oxygen in the air, in the presence of water.

One particular problem is that of children's progress towards counter-intuitive ideas. There are certain conclusions that children may draw from their direct perceptions which, though quite logical, do not accord with conventional scientific explanations: for example, that the metal part of a desk is at a lower temperature than the wooden part (it certainly feels colder). What children sense (perceptually speaking) is what makes sense to them (intellectually speaking). A better understanding of science will reveal that the explanation of the phenomenon in this example is at odds with our perceptions – it is counter-intuitive. The metal and wooden parts of the desk are both likely to be at the same temperature as the air in the room; the fact that heat energy is conducted away from fingertips more readily by the metal than by the wood produces the sensation of its being at a lower temperature. In instances such as these, children's experiences will let them down. The direct experience has to be reinterpreted in abstract terms if the occurrence is to be understood in a scientific sense.

What if children don't seem to be making progress?

Having looked at progress in its commonly used sense of moving forward, we might consider cases where children appear not to move. Even the most carefully planned activities do not necessarily bring the outcomes intended. But some of the outcomes in which children appear to stand still, go backwards, or move sideways can be seen as part of progression.

There are sure to be times when children appear to be standing still, but at these times they may be accumulating experiences, trading ideas, gathering breadth of understanding and reflecting. Yet this is progress through consolidation.

Perhaps more worrying to teachers who feel under pressure to cover all the ground and deliver children's science entitlement is the experience of children 'going backwards'. What we have in mind here is not the feeling that 'They've forgotten everything!' encountered at the beginning of each term, especially after the summer holidays; that sort of forgetting usually relates to rules and conventions which tend to be fairly quickly remembered. The concern here is with a real decline in performance which is sometimes seen in children's developing science concepts, but nevertheless is associated with a deepening of their understanding.

For example, young children may develop a good intuitive understanding of temperature mixing, gained from happy hours spent in the bath. However, during the middle years of childhood, this understanding often goes awry. This seems to be connected with the fact that children's understanding of temperature is progressing on another front – they are probably quantifying temperature, using thermometers – and the conflict between the two kinds of understanding causes a fall in performance. It is well known, for example, that many children at this age will predict that mixing two volumes of water at 30 °C will give a mixture at 60 °C, even though they know that two lots of warm water do not, when put together, make hotter water.

Sometimes we need to go backwards in order to go forwards. Progress inside an individual's head is not always visible in straightforward terms. Such reorganizations may take time. They also happen fairly regularly as new learning occurs in a cycle of:

◆ initial control of a situation, but relying on limited procedures;
◆ an attempt to generate rules of a more general nature; this may result in a more erratic performance than in the first stage, even though understanding is greater;
◆ control of the new way of thinking in practice, with increased competence and improved performance.

Moving sideways is actually quite respectable in science. Some of children's science activities take them only indirectly closer to conventional scientific understanding. This happens when children convince themselves, as the result of thinking or doing, that the idea which they had previously held must be rejected. For example, during the SPACE research some infants asserted that mice must be drinking the missing water (which had evaporated) from a water tank. However, the cheese they left out to gather proof of unseen nocturnal revels remained uneaten and the children rejected their hypothesis. Had they made progress? In a sense they had, for they had succeeded in clearing an obstruction. They were not back where they had started – where they started had been put behind them. This, surely, was progress.

Appendix

The Primary SPACE Project research reports

The reports describe the collaborative research conducted with teachers aimed at understanding the development of young children's scientific ideas. The titles in the series are as follows:

Published titles

Earth in Space

Electricity

Evaporation and condensation

Growth

Light

Materials

Processes of life

Rocks, soil and weather

Sound

Forthcoming titles

Energy

Forces

Genetics and evolution

Variety of life

Human influences on the Earth

The reports are published by Liverpool University Press. Copies are available from booksellers or:

Burston Distribution Services, Unit 2A, Newbridge Trading Estate, Newbridge Close, Off Whitby Road, Bristol BS4 4AX (tel 0117 724248, fax 0117 711056)

Index